C000258795

ALIEN RESURRECTION™

SCRIPTBOOK

Other *Alien* and *Alien Resurrection*
titles from Titan Books

The Making of Alien Resurrection
Alien Resurrection Postcard Book

Alien: The Special Effects
The Book of Alien
Giger's Alien

Coming in Spring 98:
The Complete Aliens: A Cinematic Journey

Aliens graphic novels:
Aliens: Outbreak
Aliens: Nightmare Asylum
Aliens: Female War
Aliens: Genocide
Aliens: Labyrinth
Aliens: Stronghold
Aliens: Rogue
Aliens: Harvest
Aliens: Newt's Tale
Aliens Vs Predator
Aliens Vs Predator War
Batman Vs Aliens
Superman Vs Aliens

All Titan's *Alien* and other film and TV titles are available in good
bookshops, or from Titan Books Mail Order, PO Box 54,
Desborough, Northants, NN14 2UH.
You can also telephone 01536 763 631 with your
credit card details. Please quote AR/SB.

SCRIPTBOOK

BASED ON THE MOTION PICTURE WRITTEN BY

JOSS WHEDON

TITAN BOOKS

ALIEN RESURRECTION SCRIPTBOOK
ISBN 1 85286 866 X

Published by
Titan Books
42-44 Dolben Street
London SE1 0UP

First edition November 1997
10 9 8 7 6 5 4 3 2 1

This is a work of fiction. The characters, incidents and dialogues are products of
the author's imagination and are not to be construed as real. Any resemblance to
actual events or persons, living or dead, is entirely coincidental.

British edition published by arrangement with HarperPrism, a division of
HarperCollins Publishers.

Text and photos copyright © 1997 by Twentieth Century Fox Film Corporation.
All rights reserved.
No part of this book may be used or reproduced in any way whatsoever without
written permission of the publisher, except in the case of brief quotations
embodied in critical articles and reviews. For information contact the publishers
at the address above.

Alien Resurrection™ is a trademark of Twentieth Century Fox Film Corporation.

Cover artwork courtesy of and © 1997 by Twentieth Century Fox Film
Corporation.

Designed by Colleen Davie.

British Library Cataloguing-in-Publication Data. A catalogue record for this book
is available from the British Library.

This book is sold subject to the condition that it shall not by way of trade or
otherwise, be lent, re-sold, hired out or otherwise circulated without the
publisher's prior consent in any form of binding or cover other than that in
which it is published and without a similar condition including this condition
being imposed upon the subsequent purchaser.

Printed and bound in Great Britain by MPG Books Ltd, Bodmin, Cornwall

For Kai

A L I E N
R E S U R R E C T I O N ™

RIPLEY	Sigourney Weaver
CALL	Winona Ryder
VRIESS	Dominique Pinon
JOHNER	Ron Perlman
CHRISTIE	Gary Dourdon
PEREZ	Dan Hedaya
GEDIMAN	Brad Dourif
DISTEPHANO	Raymond Cruz
PURVIS	Leland Orser
ELGYN	Michael Wincott
HILLARD	Kim Flowers
Directed by	Jean-Pierre Jeunet
Screenplay by	Joss Whedon
Producers	Bill Badalato
	Walter Hill
	David Giler
	Gordon Carroll

ALIEN
RESURRECTION™
SCRIPTBOOK

SEQ. 1—EXT. DEEP SPACE

Surrounding the U.S.S. Auriga, *a massive research vessel that sits majestically just beyond Pluto's orbit.*

SEQ. 2—INT. LAB

Instruments show a jolt in heart rate, blood pressure. We TRACK *from the cardiograph to a small cryotube. We glimpse inside an adult-sized fetal mass encased in a clear, aspic-like gel. Tubes and cables are attached to the mass, running out of the machine. As we still* CIRCLE *, the shape begins to be more coherent, till we can see what might even be a face. Eyes, shut tight. Sleeping. Dreaming.*

> GIRL'S VOICE
> My mommy said there were no monsters—no real ones—but there are.

Scientists milling about take notes, look at the thing in aspic.

THE CAMERA MOVES BACK IN—

on the cardiograph, then moves down, to show another one. Tracking a second heartbeat from within the case.

Smaller, much faster.

SEQ. 3—INT. OPERATING CHAMBER

ANGLE: RIPLEY'S CHEST—

Being cut open by a lasersaw. We see her body still has a layer of the aspic-slime clinging to it. And her skin is unnaturally blue. As we PAN *from her chest to her face, her identity is unmistakable. Around her are several men in operating masks. Cutting her is* GEDIMAN, *a young and enthusiastic scientist. One man, seemingly in charge, stands a bit off, watching. This, by the tag on his coat, is* WREN.

WREN
Careful . . . ready with the amnio . . .

His voice is soft, comforting, like the face that watches thoughtfully from behind thick glasses.

Gediman finishes cutting. Another man steps in with a clamp. Sets it. Pulls apart the chest.

GEDIMAN
There she is . . .

He says it like he's found a lost kitten. He reaches in and pulls out a sleeping, fetal, but nearly ready to burst alien. Others work at severing umbilical threads that tie it to Ripley.

GEDIMAN
Here we go.

He holds it up and others step in with the amnio, a sort of incubator filled with amniotic fluid.

The alien screams, its tiny mouth full with teeth, and wriggles out of his grasp.

WREN
Watch it!

Everybody panics—but before the thing can get completely away from him, Gediman grabs it and puts it in the amnio. Someone shuts the top rapidly. Everybody looks at each other a moment.

GEDIMAN
Well . . .

WREN
The host?

A surgeon looks at Ripley's readings.

> SURGEON
> Doing fine.

Gediman looks at Wren, hopefully. Wren nods.

> WREN
> Sew her back up.

Gediman and the surgeon get to work, as the others carefully remove the alien.

> GEDIMAN
> Well, that went as well as could be expected—

Ripley's hand lashes out, grabs the surgeon's forearm. He yells in pain as her fingers dig into him—

Ripley's eyes pop open: wide, unseeing, consciousness flooding in behind them—her whole body so rigid it shakes—

The surgeon screams, trying to pry her off, the others scrambling, knocking things over—and we hear his bone cracking.

SEQ. 4—INT. RIPLEY'S CELL

Sudden stillness.

Ripley crouches in the middle of a small, dark chamber. She is wide-eyed, staring straight ahead in a state of near catatonia. Hair tangled and wild. But at least she's not so blue as before, nor as slimy.

The only light on her comes from directly above, from a thick pane of glass in the center of the ceiling.

ANGLE: ABOVE THE CELL

A guard stands on the floor above, looking into the cell through the square of glass in the floor, directly above Ripley. We see other panes of glass lining the floor, indicating more cells below.

ANGLE: RIPLEY

She is still for a long while. Then she lifts her hands, looks at them. Touches her face, her skin. She fingers her tunic, pulls down the neck. There is a scar running along her chest. She fingers it thoughtfully.

She looks at her forearm. Tattooed near the crook of her elbow is the number eight.

She looks up, her face unreadable.

SEQ. 5—INT. LAB

Ripley is sitting on a table as Gediman draws blood from her. He deposits it in a test beaker, studies her eyes.

WREN
How's our Number Eight today?

GEDIMAN
Appears to be in good health . . .

WREN
(noticing his tone)

How good?

GEDIMAN

Extraordinary. As in, completely off our projected charts.
(shows him some photos)
Look at the scar tissue. See the recession?

> WREN

This is from—

> GEDIMAN

Yesterday!

> WREN

This is good. This is very good.

Wren approaches Ripley and studies her face with satisfaction.

> WREN

Well, it looks like you're going to make us all very prou—

She grabs his throat with dazzling speed, applying deadly pressure as she brings his face to hers. Her eyes are burning, but lost.

> RIPLEY

Why?

> GEDIMAN

Oh my god . . .

He is as wide-eyed as Wren, and he isn't having his windpipe crushed. After a moment the shock wears off and he slams his hand into the alarm: klaxons go off, red lights start flashing.

A guard rushes in, levels his weapon at Ripley. After a moment staring him down, she opens her hand. Wren falls to his knees, gasping.

The guard fires his rifle at her—a powerful electrical charge lashes out and sends her flying back into the corner.

WREN
No, no! I'm all right!

The guards keep their weapons—"burners," these shockrifles are called—leveled at Ripley. She has recovered from the shock quickly, and sits crumpled in the corner, looking at nothing in particular.

RIPLEY
(wearily)
Why . . . ?

SEQ. 6—INT. OBSERVATION ROOM

Wren and Gediman watch through a one-way mirror as a scientist tests Ripley.

With them is GENERAL PEREZ, *the ship captain. Ramrod straight and gruff, he stares at Ripley suspiciously.*

ANGLE: RIPLEY

She is restrained, iron collar and cuffs linked to cables that anchor her to the chair. Despite the high-tech, the whole get-up seems almost medieval.

Two armed guards flank her. The scientist sits across the table, clearly a bit nervous.

ANGLE: PEREZ

He watches as the scientist holds up cards with pictures on them: house, dog, boat. Ripley gives answers we can't hear through the glass, looking pissed off and bored.

WREN
It's unprecedented.

GEDIMAN
Totally! She's operating at a completely adult capacity.

PEREZ
And her memories?

WREN
There are gaps. And there's some degree of cognitive dissonance.

GEDIMAN
She's freaked.

Wren shoots Gediman a stern look. He doesn't approve of his unscientific parlance.

WREN
"It" has some connective difficulties. A kind of low level emotional autism. Certain reactions . . .

PEREZ
But "it" remembers. Why?

WREN
I'm guessing, but . . . collective memory. Passed down generationally, at a genetic level, by the aliens. Almost like a highly evolved form of instinct. An unexpected benefit of genetic crossing.

PEREZ
(mockingly)
Benefit . . .

Perez looks at Ripley through the glass, then exits the room.

SEQ. 7—INT. CORRIDOR—CONTINUOUS

CAMERA DOLLIES OUT, PRECEDING THEM—

Perez strides along. The two scientists follow, pace him as he strides down toward a second observation room.

> GEDIMAN
> You're not thinking termination?

> PEREZ
> Oh, *boy*, am I thinking termination.

> WREN
> We don't perceive this as a problem.

> PEREZ
> Ellen Ripley died trying to wipe this species out of
> existence and for all intents and purposes succeeded.
> (getting in Wren's face)
> I'm not anxious to see her picking up her old hobbies.

> WREN
> It won't happen.

> GEDIMAN
> (grinning)
> Comes down to a fight. I'm not sure whose side she'd
> be on.

> PEREZ
> And I'm supposed to take comfort in that?

Perez stops in front of a door. He punches in a code and breathes into a little breathaliser.

The little lights blink furiously, indicating the ongoing analysis. The door to the observation room opens. They enter.

SEQ. 8—INT. OBSERVATION ROOM TWO

Darker and quieter than the other. Perez turns to the others.

> PEREZ
> Bottom line is, she looks at me funny and I put her down. As far as I'm concerned, Number Eight is a meat by-product. This girl here is the money.

He looks into another cell. In the darkness we can barely make out the outline of an alien head. A really big one.

> PEREZ
> How soon before she's producing?

> WREN
> Days. Less, maybe. We'll need the cargo.

> PEREZ
> It's on its way.

ANGLE: THE QUEEN'S POV—

Looking back through the glass at the three men. As they stare at the Queen, the SHOT PULLS UP AND BACK, *the Queen rearing to her full height. The whole room becomes visible, and we see that there are no fewer than eight guards in here with them, standing post silent around the cage.*

SEQ. 9—INT. MESS HALL

Ripley is seated across from Gediman. She is still chained, though with enough mobility to eat comfortably.

Gediman is eating at a good pace, but Ripley has stopped eating. She is staring at her fork, turning it over in her hand, in her mind.

GEDIMAN

"Fork."

The memory comes back. She shakes her head wearily.

RIPLEY
(softly)

Fuck . . .

GEDIMAN
(pretending to correct her)

"Fork."

She smiles imperceptibly, then the smile fades. After a moment:

RIPLEY

How did you . . .

GEDIMAN

How did we get you? Hard work. Blood samples, taken on Fiori 16, on ice.

RIPLEY

Fiori 16 . . .

GEDIMAN

Ring a bell? What do you remember about that place?

She thinks—and puts her hand to her hair, almost as if to check if it's there. Thinks some more.

RIPLEY

Came down the shuttle . . . it was cold . . . they didn't make it. They didn't survive.

GEDIMAN

Who?

She thinks, hard, but the names don't come.

RIPLEY

I can see their faces, but . . . there's a girl . . .

GEDIMAN ·

What else?

RIPLEY

The cold . . . and . . .
(touches her chest)
. . . the pain.

She looks up at him.

RIPLEY

Does "it" . . . grow?

GEDIMAN

Does "it" . . . ? Yeah. Rapidly.

RIPLEY

It's a Queen.

GEDIMAN

How did you know that?

RIPLEY
It'll breed. You'll die. Everyone in the . . . fucking . . .
(searches for the word, then spits it out)
. . . company. Will die.

GEDIMAN
Company?

WREN
(O.S.)
Weyland Yutani.

He has entered behind her and comes up to the table.

WREN
Our Ripley's former employers. Terran Growth con-
glom, had some defense contracts under the military.
Before your time, Gediman—they went under decades
ago, bought out by Walmart. Fortunes of war.
(to Ripley)
You'll find things have changed a good deal since your
time.

RIPLEY
I doubt that.

WREN
We're not flying blind here, you know. This is the
United Systems military, not some greedy corporation.

RIPLEY
It won't make any . . . difference . . .

*She stops a moment, puzzled at the familiarity of the sentence, then
continues:*

RIPLEY

You're still gonna die.

WREN

And how do you feel about that?

RIPLEY
(shrugs)

It's your funeral.

WREN

I wish you could understand what we're trying to do here.
The potential benefits of this race go way beyond urban
pacification. New alloys, new vaccines . . . there's nothing
like this in any world we've seen. You should be very
proud.

She laughs bitterly.

RIPLEY

Oh, I am.

WREN

And the animals themselves are wondrous. They'll be
invaluable once we've harnessed them.

RIPLEY

It's a cancer. You can't teach it tricks.

*This stops Wren, and he retreats silently. Ripley repeats a word to
herself, thinking.*

RIPLEY

"Them . . ."

SEQ. 10—EXT. DEEP SPACE

We see the Auriga *far in the distance. Suddenly, another ship roars into frame, heading for the* Auriga.

A small vessel, it is every bit as dirty and jerry-rigged as the Auriga *is pristine. To accentuate the difference, the sudden roar of its engines is accompanied by heavy, thrashing rock music.*

As it passes, we see a painting on the fuselage: a classic bomber cheesecake, a semi-clad wonderbabe riding a rocket, with the legend BETTY *above her head.*

SEQ. 11—INT. COCKPIT OF THE *BETTY*—CONTINUOUS

The music is coming from nearby. Piloting the ship toward the Auriga *is* HILLARD, *a rough-skinned woman in her forties. Behind her stands* ELGYN, *the leader of the group. He has the kind of authority that doesn't need to flaunt itself. Maybe fifty, by the silver in his hair. He speaks into the vidcom.*

ELGYN
(good naturedly)
My authorization code is "fuck you," son. Now open
the goddamn bay or General Perez is gonna do a
Wichita stomp on your virgin ass.
(he switches off)
I guarantee that boy's never seen the inside of a woman.
(to Hillard)
Bring us in on three-oh descent, ride the parallel.

HILLARD
Darlin' it's done.

ELGYN
Don't cut thrust till six hundred meters. Give 'em a little
fright.

He puts his hand on her shoulder, runs it up along her cheek as he exits. They're more than just friends.

He moves through a hallway, sticks his head in a cubicle.

> ELGYN
> Christie! Rise and shine. We're docking.

He proceeds into:

SEQ. 12—INT. HALLWAY—CONTINUOUS

CHRISTIE *is up and mostly dressed. He is black, very large, and has a distinctly military bearing. He speaks with quiet, don't-fuck-with-me authority. He is strapping a contraption to his forearm, like a mechanical pulley equipped with a weapon. Elgyn comes over to join him.*

> CHRISTIE
> What's our status?

> ELGYN
> We're coming in. Time to enjoy a little of the General's hospitality.

> CHRISTIE
> Oh, great. Army food.

> ELGYN
> It'll keep us till we can get the family wagon up to spec. Assuming the natives are friendly.

> CHRISTIE
> We expecting any trouble?

ELGYN
From Perez? I doubt it. Still, let's be ever vigilant.

SEQ. 13—INT. CARGO BAY—CONTINUOUS

Lying on a gurney-like steel dolly, working under a machine, is VRIESS, *chief mechanic.*

CALL *brings down a trolley by means of a magnetic chain hoist.*

CAMERA DOLLIES UP AND OVER THE ENGINE BLOCK, PAST A BALCONY OVERLOOKING IT

On the railing leans JOHNER. *He is thickset, mean, and ugly, with scars crisscrossing his ugly bald head. In his hand is a throwing knife.*

He lets it play along his fingers, looking down at Vriess. He's right above Vriess's exposed legs. He holds the knife over Vriess's crotch. Smiling, he balances the knife on the palm of his hand, and then—

As Call looks up and sees—

He lets it fall.

CALL
No!

She jumps down—the knife falls, spinning—she races for Vriess— the knife falls—

And lands, sticking solidly into Vriess's upper thigh.

ANGLE: VRIESS—

Continues to work, humming to himself. Completely oblivious.

Johner laughs as Call looks up at him, fury crossing her face.

CALL
What is wrong with you?

JOHNER
Just a little target practice. Vriess isn't complaining.

Vriess hears, looks down and sees the knife sticking out of his leg.

He wheels out from under the machine in a second flat.

VRIESS
Goddamnit!

He hits a lever the back of his dolly flies up, transforming it into a wheelchair.

VRIESS
Johner! You son of a whore.

Johner climbs down to where the others are, smiling smugly. Call pulls the knife out of Vriess's leg. Vriess doesn't flinch. From all appearances, his legs are numb.

JOHNER
Oh, come on, you didn't feel a thing.

CALL
(to Johner)
You are an inbred motherfucker, you know that?

JOHNER
I'll take that knife back now.

CALL
Where do you want it?

Call stares at him, knife out. She's really pissed.

> VRIESS
>
> Call, forget it. He's been sucking down too much homebrew.

> JOHNER
>
> The knife?

Call jams the knife between two metal blocks and snaps the blade off. Johner gets in her face.

> JOHNER
>
> Don't push me, little Annalee. You hang with us a while, you'll learn I'm not the man with whom to fuck.

A moment. She doesn't flinch, doesn't move. He exits, full of annoying bravado.

> VRIESS
>
> We really have to start associating with a better class of people. Get back in the grid, give me a sequence run.

He hits a level, dropping the chair back down to a gurney, and wheels back under.

SEQ. 14—EXT. *AURIGA* DOCKING BAY

A panel opens to welcome the proportionally tiny ship. The bay is on the bottom of the Auriga—*the doors are actually over the* Betty, *which rises into the airlock.*

SEQ. 15—INT. AIRLOCK

The outer doors close under the ship. Pressurized air shoots into the airlock for a few seconds, and then the inner doors open, the ship rising into the bay.

SEQ. 16—INT. DOCKING BAY

The Betty comes into position along the dock, the airlock doors closing under it. Enormous electromagnets rise from the dock and position themselves against the Betty's hull, docking it against the quay in a great clanging of metal.

SEQ. 17—INT. CORRIDOR

The ship takes up most of the dock area—the rest stretching forth in a long platform to the entrance.

Three soldiers in full armor stand rigid on the platform, waiting. Others mill about, working.

The hatch atop the ship slowly opens. One by one the crew files out of the Betty. Seeing them together, we realize what sets them apart from this new environment: They're not in uniform. They're an eclectic, fiercely individualist group. Their clothes colorful yet still utilitarian. Even Vriess's wheelchair is noticeable as it rolls down the platform.

What they have in common is the toughness, the wary eyes, leathery skin. They're ready to kill and it shows. These guys are smugglers. A long time ago we'd have called them pirates.

All six of them emerge, looking around them. They file past the silent, uniformed soldiers. The last one suddenly puts a hand on Johner's jacket, stops him. There is a bulge under it. A sensor light on the back of the soldier's glove blinks when he touches the bulge.

> SOLDIER
> No projectile weaponry is allowed on board the vessel, sir.

Johner opens his jacket, shows what he's packing: a large thermos.

JOHNER

Moonshine—my own. Way more dangerous.

SOLDIER

Sorry, sir.

Elgyn comes toward him and looks up.

ELGYN

What, do you think we're going to hijack the vessel? All six of us?

PEREZ
(entering)

No, I think one of your asshole crew is going to get drunk and put a bullet through the hull. We are in *space*, Elgyn.

He motions for the crew to follow him. Vriess, in turn, comes up to the soldier.

VRIESS

Wanna check the chair?

The soldier signals him to move along.

SEQ. 18—INT. PEREZ'S CHAMBERS—LATER

ANGLE: MONEY

A stack of bills is dropped down on a desk, then another. They're green, identifiably money, but they're square, about the size of cocktail napkins. The face on them is unfamiliar. They are thousand dollar bills.

WIDER ANGLE—

A good sized suite, decorated in a sparse, military fashion. Perez is behind his desk, the money sitting between him and Elgyn.

PEREZ

This wasn't easy to come by.

ELGYN

Neither was our cargo. You're not pleading poverty, are you?

PEREZ

We're well funded. I mean the bills. There's not many that still deal in coin.

ELGYN

Just the ones that don't like their every transaction recorded. The fringe element. I guess that would include you, though, wouldn't it?

PEREZ

Drink?

ELGYN

Constantly. I'm guessing whatever you've got going here isn't exactly approved by Congress.

He tears off the protective covering of a little plastic container (like a cartridge for printer ink), pours out a solid brown cube into a glass, and passes the glass under a laser for a split second. The cube has liquefied.

PEREZ
(changing the subject)
Where'd you pick up the new fish?

ELGYN

Call? Out by the handle, she was looking for a
maintenance gig.

PEREZ

Makes an impression.

ELGYN

She is severely fuckable, isn't she? And the very devil
with a socket wrench. I think Vriess somewhat pines.

He takes a stack of bills, smells it. He likes the smell.

ELGYN

She is curious about this little transaction. You can
hardly blame her. Awfully cloak and dagger . . .

Perez hands a drink to Elgyn.

PEREZ

This is an army operation.

ELGYN

Most army research labs don't have to operate outside
regulated space. And they don't call for the kind of
cargo we brought.

PEREZ

Do you want something, Elgyn?

ELGYN

Just bed and board, couple of days worth. Vriess'll want
to snag a few spare parts. If we're not imposing.

PEREZ
Not at all. Keep out of the restricted areas, don't start
any fights, and mi casa is yours, too.

Elgyn raises his glass.

PEREZ
I trust, of course, that you can mind your own business.

ELGYN
(smiles)
I'm famous for it.

They drink.

SEQ. 19—INT. DOCKING BAY—LATER

Four soldiers and two scientists stand at the foot of the Betty, *below
the platform the crew came off on. A bottom hatch slowly opens, a
ramp lowering to the floor.*

*From within comes the "cargo", a metal box about six feet long and
eight high. It rolls down slowly on a long dolly. Call emerges with
it, gently pushing it along.*

*Behind her, Johner pushes a second, identical box out. One of the
soldiers motions for them to follow him, and they do.*

Call watches everything intently, distrustfully.

SEQ. 20—INT. CORRIDOR BY LABS—A BIT LATER

Two guards stand before the door marked RESTRICTED AREA. *When
they see the dollies approaching, they knock on the door. It opens.
Wren is waiting inside.*

*Call and Johner wheel the boxes to the door. They are about to go
through when the guards silently step in their way. They step back*

as the soldiers take possession of the boxes and wheel the cargo through.

Call watches as the door slides shut.

SEQ. 21—INT. A CHAMBER—MOMENTS LATER

The transparent cover of one of the metal boxes opens.

Camera dollies out—

We discover little by little the metal boxes placed side by side. Glass covers open up as the metal boxes straighten up.

Cryotubes. People sleeping inside.

One by one the tubes are hauled to one side of the room as the second unit is wheeled in. By the end there are ten people sleeping side by side in their tubes in the dark chamber.

The scientist meanwhile retires to:

SEQ. 22—INT. AN ADJOINING CHAMBER—CONTINUOUS

With a long glass window looking at the chamber.

The last of the soldiers leaves the chamber and we see the door lock behind them. Wren starts working his computer screen.

The glass tops of the cryotubes slide open. We see temperature and lifesign gauges begin to change.

There is a thick whirring as a part of the ceiling above the tubes lowers, lowers, and rotates slowly.

Stuck to the other side of it are ten alien eggs. The ceiling rotates just enough so that they are aimed at the heads of the sleepers.

For a moment nothing happens.

One of the sleeper's eyes flutters slightly. Opens.

All ten eggs open simultaneously.

SEQ. 23—INT. CONFERENCE HALL

A huge room, used for assemblies and events. It has a chain basketball net set up at one end, crude court lines taped to the floor. Ripley stands beneath the net with a ball, dribbling absently. Only her wrists are chained here.

At the other end are set up tables and folding chairs. The crew of the Betty, *sans Elgyn, are filing in to eat here.*

Johner spies Ripley and smiles at her.

> JOHNER
>
> Ooh.

Johner comes up to Ripley. Her expression makes it clear how much she enjoys having him in her face.

> JOHNER
>
> How about a little one on one?

She keeps dribbling, says nothing.

> JOHNER
>
> What do you say?

> RIPLEY
>
> Get away from me!

> JOHNER
>
> Why should I?

RIPLEY
Because pain hurts.

He falters a moment at her quiet threat, then:

JOHNER
Are you gonna hurt me then? I think I might enjoy that.

He gives her an ugly smile. She gives him one right back.

She hits him solidly in the chest with both hands—and he flies back ten feet, landing badly on a group of chairs.

His mates fly into action, Christie grabs a standing ashtray—Hillard jumps Ripley from behind.

She throws her off with ease. Hits her in the stomach with the basketball.

Christie swings at her with the ashtray and smashes her right in the face. She arcs back . . . reaches into her mouth and pulls out a bloody tooth. Christie hesitates, suddenly not sure she should have done that.

She's at Christie's throat before he has a chance to react, squeezing, battling away the ashtray—Johner comes at her again and she leaps on him, throws him to the ground, snarling. Like she's gonna rip his throat out with her teeth.

WREN
Ripley—

Ripley looks up and four guards are pointing burners on her. Wren and Gediman behind them.

Call, standing to one side of Vriess, reacts visibly to the name.

Everyone slowly backs off. Christie stands with his hands behind his back, as if concealing something.

Call watches in rapt silence.

> WREN
>
> Don't let's have a scene.

Ripley lets go of Johner, stands.

> RIPLEY
>
> He . . . smells.

> JOHNER
> (barely breathing)
> What the hell are you?

She looks down on him—in both senses of the phrase. Looks around at everyone staring at her. She spits a bit of blood from her mouth and exits, scooping up the basketball and easily sailing it into the basket as she goes.

> WREN
> (to Gediman)
> She is something of a predator, isn't she?

> GEDIMAN
>
> Well . . . the guy does smell . . .

The few drops of blood she spit sizzle on the floor—not eating through, but melting a small patch.

SEQ. 24—EXT. *AURIGA*

The vessel floats majestically in the starry blackness of space as the sun disappears behind Pluto.

SEQ. 25—INT. HILLARD AND ELGYN'S ROOM—NIGHT

Hillard is lying in bed, breathing heavily, giving out little moans of pleasure.

It's not what we thought. In fact, Elgyn is massaging the bottoms of her feet.

SEQ. 26—INT. PEREZ'S CHAMBERS

A hand with a little laser wand reaches out to a shoe wax container; the wax bursts into flame.

Perez waxes his boots—melting the wax himself, according to army regulations.

SEQ. 27—INT. SPARE PARTS CORRIDOR

Vriess is rolling about the Auriga's engine room, rummaging through bins for spare parts. He has a handful of bolts, wires, and such.

SEQ. 28—INT. MESS HALL

Christie, Call, and Johner, all watching a video in the mess hall.

SEQ. 29—INT. OBSERVATION ROOM—NIGHT

A sleep cycle is indicated by the low lighting and the near emptiness of the room. Gediman alone is in here, writing observations down in a notebook as he watches the pen.

Inside are three aliens, barely visible in the shadows. Two of them seem to be hibernating, curled up in the corner, but the third faces the glass, tilting its head and hissing at it. Gediman sits right up close to it, his face just inches away from the beast's.

It draws back its lip and opens its mouth. The metallic tongue issues slowly forth, dripping with slime.

> GEDIMAN
> (softly fascinated)
> Is that a distended externus lingua . . . or are you just
> happy to see me?

He presses his face against the glass, like a kid outside a candy store. The alien shoots its tongue at him, thwacking the glass hard.

Gediman backs off and, without tearing his eyes away from the cage, pushes a big red fail-safe button.

Jets of liquid nitrogen squirt toward the monster, forcing it back to the middle of its cage, screaming. The jets turn off.

After a moment the alien starts for the glass again. Gediman reaches his hand out for the red fail-safe button. The beast freezes.

His hand remains frozen above the button.

> GEDIMAN
> (to the alien)
> Fast learner, huh?

SEQ. 30—INT. MESS HALL—NIGHT

Christie, Call, and Johner are still watching the TV. They are decently drunk by now, trading sips of Johner's wretched homebrew.

On the screen is a gun, advertised on the Home Shopping Network.

Call takes a big swig—not her first—from Johner's thermos, makes a face. She tries to stand up, takes a spill over her chair. The others laugh.

> CALL
> Jesus, Johner, what do you put in that shit, battery acid?

> JOHNER
> Just for coloring.

> CHRISTIE
> You're not gonna stay and watch? This is a powerful drama.

> CALL
> (shakes her head)
> I'm tapped. I'm sleeping.

She stumbles out of the room.

> JOHNER
> The bitches can't handle the brew.

SEQ. 31—INT. CORRIDOR

As soon as she's left the room, Call straightens up, perfectly sober. She glances around, then walks down the hallway.

She gets to a door leading to the restricted area. Locked. She looks around, digs into her pocket. She pulls out a small container, looks kind of like a respirator. She looks around—sinking back into the shadows as two guards pass in the next hall—and faces the door.

She begins punching in code with impressive speed and surety. When the screen next to it flashes, she "breathes" into the breathaliser by spraying it.

It takes a minute, but it works. The locks clack open, the door rises silently before her.

SEQ. 32—INT. CELLBLOCK—MOMENTS LATER

Call pads silently down the corridor, looking for one cell.

SEQ. 33—RIPLEY'S CELL—CONTINUOUS

The cell door opens silently. Call hesitates a moment, then slips in, shutting the door behind her.

BOOM DOWN—

Ripley is asleep, still in a squatting position in the middle of the room. Call approaches.

She stares down at Ripley a moment. A shadow passes as a guard walks above them, Call tenses until he is gone. Looks back down at Ripley—still sleeping.

Call extends her hand, flexes her wrist. The meanest looking stiletto you've ever seen extends from out of her sleeve. It's gotta be a foot long, and sharp enough to shave with.

She raises her hand to punch it through Ripley's heart.

Ripley shifts slightly. Call stops.

ANGLE: RIPLEY'S CHEST

Ripley's shirt is open enough to show a good portion of the scar.

Call hesitates, staring, realization flooding her face.

                    RIPLEY
    Well?

Call starts, moving back a pace.

                    RIPLEY
    You gonna kill me or what?

CALL
There's no point, is there?

A flick of her wrist and the stiletto whips back up her sleeve. Ripley sits up.

CALL
It's already out of you. Christ . . . Is it here? Is it on board?

RIPLEY
(smiling)
You mean my baby?

CALL
I don't understand. If they've got it, why are they keeping you alive?

RIPLEY
Curious. I'm the latest thing.

CALL
Those sick bastards.

She raises her arm, the stiletto gliding out again.

CALL
I can make it stop. The pain . . . this nightmare. It's all I can offer you.

Ripley holds her palm up, presses it against the point of the blade.

RIPLEY
What makes you think I would let you do that?

Ripley pushes her hand out—the blade goes right through her palm—she keeps pushing her hand out slowly, a good five inches of the blade sticking out of the back of her hand before she stops. Call stares at her.

CALL

What are you?

RIPLEY

Ripley, Ellen, Lieutenant first class, number 36706.

CALL

Ellen Ripley died two hundred years ago.

Ripley pulls her hand back suddenly, grimacing at the pain.

RIPLEY

What do you know about it?

CALL

I've read Morse—I've read all the banned histories. She gave her life to protect us from the beast. You're not her.

RIPLEY

I'm not her? What am I then?

CALL

You're a thing. A construct. They grew you in a fucking lab.

RIPLEY

But only God can make a tree.

CALL
And now they've brought the beast out of you.

RIPLEY
(smiling)
Not all the way out.

CALL
What?

RIPLEY
It's in my head, behind my eyes. I can hear it moving.

The smile is gone, some real vulnerability showing through. Call softens, trying a different tack.

CALL
Help me. If there's anything human in you at all, help me stop them before this thing gets loose.

RIPLEY
It's already loose.

Call's expression changes. Those words terrify her, but she's not sure if Ripley means what she thinks.

Ripley raises her hand at Call's head—Call flinches—but Ripley stops a few inches away. Then touches her forehead gently, almost sensually.

RIPLEY
Once the thought . . . the hope for it . . . grows here . . . then it's found its way. It will come because . . . they'll bring it. Bring it forth.

CALL
You want that.

RIPLEY
I've come to terms with the fact of it. It's inevitable.

CALL
Not as long as there's breath in me.

RIPLEY
You'll never get out of here alive.

CALL
(unconvincingly)
I don't care.

RIPLEY
Don't you?

Ripley lashes out and grabs Call by the throat. Call swings with the blade but Ripley has her arm pinned before she can connect. Ripley squeezes the girl's neck.

Ripley looks at Call with a world of sadness.

RIPLEY
I can make it stop . . .

Call's eyes are pleading, terrified.

Ripley finally lets go, and she drops to the ground, gasping for air.

RIPLEY
Go. They're coming for you.

As soon as she can move, Call gets up and scrambles for the door.

SEQ. 34—INT. CORRIDOR OUTSIDE RIPLEY'S CELL—CONTINUOUS

Call comes out and before she can move, a rifle butt hits her in the head. She goes down but not out as two guards grab her. Wren is with them and three more.

> WREN
> I think you're gonna find that this was ill-advised.
> (to the guards)
> Where are her friends?

> GUARD
> Mess hall, most of them.

> WREN
> Sound the alarm. I want them rounded up—now!

SEQ. 35—INT. MESS HALL—MOMENTS LATER

Elgyn and Hillard are pushed into the room, sleepy and confused. Christie and Johner are being herded in by soldiers. Call is thrown into the group as well.

> ELGYN
> What the fuck is going on here?

> CHRISTIE
> It looks like a double-cross, boss.

> WREN
> Where is the other one? With the chair?

                    JOHNER
                  (to a soldier)
Get your fucking hands off me!

                    ELGYN
Doctor, talk to me. What's going on?

                    WREN
You're gonna tell me who you're working for right now
or you'll be screaming it come sunrise.

                    CALL
Wren, they got nothing to do with this.

                    HILLARD
To do with what?

                    ELGYN
Everybody calm down. We can work this out, there's no
need to get emotional . . .

SUPER FAST DOLLY IN ON CHRISTIE—

Standing still, his hands behind his back.

*As Elgyn speaks, two guns slip out of Christie's sleeves into his
hands, thanks to the pulley system we saw him set up.*

                    WREN
Do you know what the penalties for terrorist activity
are?

                    JOHNER
Terrorist?

ELGYN

There's no goddamn terrorists on my crew. Call, what's this about?

WREN

I don't give a shit if you're in on this or not. You brought a subversive onto a military vessel and as far as I'm concerned you fry with her. You hear me?

ELGYN

I do. Christie?

With lightning precision, Christie raises his hands and blows two of the guards away. He takes out a third to his left without even looking that way.

One guard gets off a shot with his burner before Call's elbow knocks his teeth well into his throat.

Christie tackles the next guard as Johner presses a latch on the bottom of his thermos. The top half flies off revealing the handle of a gun inside—he grabs it as another guard runs up. Johner doesn't have time to pull the gun out of the thermos so he shoots right through it, sending the guard flying.

Elgyn pulls a sawed-off shotgun from under his jacket. There's not one of these guys that isn't carrying.

SEQ. 36—INT. OBSERVATION LAB—CONTINUOUS

Alarms, flashing red lights. Gediman looking in a video monitor.

GEDIMAN

Oh, man . . . You three! Go! Sector two.

All but one of the guards rush out to investigate. Gediman works the surveillance screen, trying to see what's happening.

SEQ. 37—INT. MESS HALL—CONTINUOUS

When the smoke clears, there are two guards still standing. They point their weapons ineffectually.

Johner has a gun to Wren's head and a gun on the guards, who are also covered by Hillard.

> ELGYN
> Nice and easy, boys . . .

Call starts to take off.

> CALL
> I'm gonna finish this.

Elgyn grabs her by the hair, roughly pulls her back.

> ELGYN
> You're going nowhere, Annalee.

SEQ. 38—INT. OBSERVATION LAB—CONTINUOUS

ANGLE: IN THE PEN

The three aliens have picked up the energy, are stalking back and forth like tigers in the dim light of their pen.

ANGLE: THEIR POV

We see Gediman and the guard, their backs to us. PAN OVER *to the fail-safe button, safely out of Gediman's reach.*

The aliens stop pacing. One of them, to the right, looks over at the one on the left. Something passes between them. They look back at the humans. At each other.

They set on the middle alien, tearing it apart. It lets out a piercing, insectile shriek as they tear it limb from limb.

Gediman spins in terror, the guard bringing up his weapon— Gediman hits the lights inside the pen and as they blink to the shocking brightness we see the remains of the third alien on the ground as a giant pool of its blood eats a hole in the floor.

> GEDIMAN
> Oh, God—

He bolts for the fail-safe but it's too late—the blood eats all the way through. The two aliens dive through the hole just as Gediman hits the button—freezing gas fills the chamber but there's nothing to freeze.

> GEDIMAN
> No no no!

He hits another sequence and the door slides open. He rushes in, kneels by the hole and looks down.

ANGLE: HIS POV

Their blood has already eaten through two levels.

> GEDIMAN
> Christ. They could be anywhere.

He looks up at the guard—and an alien flies up at him through the hole. It was hanging on the ceiling below and it pulls him through before he can breathe a decent scream. The guard just stares, shaking.

SEQ. 39—INT. MESS HALL

The Mexican standoff is getting even more heated. Call faces Elgyn, urgently explaining.

CALL
He's conducting illegal experiments. He's breeding—

JOHNER
She's a goddamn mole! Ice the bitch—

CALL
Listen to me! He's breeding a deadly alien species in there. Beyond toxic. If they get loose, it'll make the Lacerta Worm Plague look like a fucking square dance.

CHRISTIE
Listen.

Far away we hear screaming. Everyone stops. Wren turns slowly in the direction of the noise.

WREN
No . . .

SEQ. 40—INT. OBSERVATION LAB

Terrified, a soldier passes cages now empty of aliens. All the glass is broken. Soldiers' bodies are strewn on the floor.

Slowly, he musters up the courage to approach one of the cages. Sticks his head inside.

Nothing is visible in the dark. The soldier steps inside, alert.

ANGLE: THE RED BUTTON—

That controls the gas jets. It is big in the foreground as in the background, the soldier enters the pen. Suddenly an alien tongue punches the button, hitting the jets.

ANGLE: IN THE PEN

The soldier screams as the gas freezes him—his arm breaks off, the other stuck to his screaming face. He's dead and brittle as he hits the floor.

SEQ. 41—INT. RIPLEY'S CELL—CONTINUOUS

Ripley sits in the dark, the noise of chaos starting to filter in.

CAMERA TURNS SLOWLY AROUND HER

She can't help it, she laughs.

SEQ. 42—INT. LIFEBOAT BAY ONE—CONTINUOUS

Men are rushing into one of the lifeboats. They sit facing each other in the tiny vessel and strap themselves in. Perez is there, hurrying the soldiers in.

                         PEREZ
          Bay three! Go!

An alien suddenly leaps into it, starts feeding on the men strapped down—they are screaming. Perez rolls in a grenade. The doors shut and Perez hits the eject button.

SEQ. 43—EXT. *AURIGA*—CONTINUOUS

The lifeboat is ejected from the Auriga.

ANGLE: PEREZ—

Triggers the remote control for the grenade.

ANGLE: THE VESSEL—

Explodes.

SEQ. 44—INT. LIFEBOAT BAY ONE—CONTINUOUS

Perez watches the explosion with stolid grief. An alien rises behind him.

SEQ. 45—INT. MESS HALL—CONTINUOUS

The noise of the explosion outside—and of a few inside as well— resounds all around. Father's voice still urges evacuation.

                    WREN
    No!
                (to Call)
    What have you done?

                    CALL
                (remorseful)
    Nothing.

                    ELGYN
    All right. We make for the *Betty*.

                    HILLARD
    Betty's all the way across the ship! Who knows what's in
    between.

A guard, DISTEPHANO, steps forward.

                    DISTEPHANO
                (to Wren)
    Sir, we have to go.
                (to Elgyn)
    Let him go. No quarrel.

ELGYN
You can have him when we're off. Not before.

They start out, dragging Wren along. Guns still on Call and the soldiers.

HILLARD
What about Vriess?

JOHNER
Fuck Vriess!

SEQ. 46—INT. CORRIDOR—CONTINUOUS

Vriess enters, looking around. He is getting wigged, although none of the trouble is here. Emergency lights pulse along the floor, urging him toward the exit.

FATHER
Evacuate immediately. All decks. This is not a drill.

A drop of something lands on his leg. It takes him a moment to notice that it's eating right through. He looks up, backing slowly away.

Something stirs in the rafters. Coiled about the pipes.

Vriess looks at it, momentarily puzzled. Then we see the beast's shadow cover him as it lowers itself.

He reaches for the chair and from the arms of it he pulls out pieces of hardware that he quickly assembles into a shotgun. Blows the beast away.

SEQ. 47—INT. RIPLEY'S CELL/CORRIDOR

Aliens begin banging against the vent of the cell—it won't hold much longer. Ripley stands at the door, looking it over.

She punches the locking panel, bending the metal and smashing the blinking lights. Looks at her hand—her knuckles bleed only slightly.

Punches again and then rips the panel off, pulls out the wiring. We hear the click of the door unlocking.

The air vent panel bursts partially out of the wall, screws flying across the room.

Ripley pulls the door open and steps into the hall. Moving quickly down the empty corridor, she rounds the corner.

SEQ. 48—INT. CORRIDOR—CONTINUOUS

The crew walks along, moving fast but cautiously. They pass a corridor with a window at the end, come to a fork in the hall.

> CHRISTIE
>
> Which way?

> WREN
>
> I'm not sure.
> (pointing to one)
> This is faster but if there's been a breach it'll be closed off.

ANGLE: ELGYN

He is near the rear. As he passes an adjoining hallway he stops suddenly, hesitates, and then enters.

CAMERA DOLLIES IN AT GROUND LEVEL

There is a gun on the floor some ten yards away.

> ELGYN
>
> Very nice . . .

He walks over and picks it up.

ELGYN
No projectile weaponry, huh?

CAMERA DOLLIES OUT

He looks a bit further down the hall. Sitting on the floor is a cherry-looking shotgun. Elgyn makes for it. As he approaches, we see the shotgun is sitting near a hole in the floor, melted by alien blood.

Call enters the hall as Elgyn gets near the shotgun. She is instantly suspicious.

CALL
Elgyn . . .

ELGYN
Forget it, Annalee. You're not one of us—you don't carry.
(picking up the gun)
I think this one's for me.

CALL
Elgyn . . .

ELGYN
I told you—

CALL
Who put that gun there?

He stops. Turns back to look at her, her point sinking in. Slowly he turns back to look down in the hole.

An alien drops on him from above.

He barely has time to scream as it grabs him, holds him fast, bringing its head to his chest.

His new shotgun clatters to the floor, falling into the hole.

The alien's tongue shoots out—

ANGLE: ELGYN'S HEART

Like a medical film, we see his heart pumping in slow motion, then the tongue bursts right through it.

ANGLE: CALL—

Paralyzed. She is a good fifteen feet away, but Elgyn's heart's blood still splatters her face.

The rest of the crew comes charging down the hall, stops at the sight.

> HILLARD
> Elgyn!

The alien drops Elgyn. He falls over the hole as the alien starts slowly toward Call. She cannot move, cannot take her eyes off it.

> JOHNER
> Shoot it!

> CHRISTIE
> Call, move!

> JOHNER
> Oh, for chrissake—

He is about to fire at both of them but Distephano stops him.

DISTEPHANO
The window! You wanna die?

The window is framed right behind the alien. No shot.

JOHNER
Then let's go!

CHRISTIE
Call!

She can't move. The alien creeps slowly toward her, then stops. Turns.

ANGLE: ELGYN'S BODY—

Moves slightly.

The alien goes slowly back to him, sniffingly.

It cranes its head at him. His face, still very much dead. His belly.

ANGLE: ELGYN'S STOMACH

Through the wound, the end of Elgyn's shotgun pokes through.

And blasts the beast in the face.

It arcs back, slamming into the ground. Acidic blood peppers the ceiling.

Call and the crew look on with shocked wonder, waiting to see what's coming next.

ANGLE: THE HOLE

For a moment, nothing. Then Ripley pulls herself easily out of the hole, looking about her with calm clarity, the shotgun in one hand. Looks at Call, who still hasn't taken a breath, let alone a step.

RIPLEY
Was it everything you'd hoped?

That sort of snaps Call out of it, and she lets out a shuddering breath.

Ripley kneels by the dead alien. Looks at it contemplatively, cocking her head. Runs her hand along its black, smooth head—the part that wasn't blown off. Hillard stops several feet away, unwilling to go too close to the prostrate beast. The rest of the crew gather about her, looking at Ripley.

CHRISTIE
Okay . . . real slow now. What. The. Fuck.

ANGLE: HILLARD—

Kneeling by Elgyn's body. No tears, but terribly quiet.

JOHNER
What do we do?

CHRISTIE
Same thing we were doing. We leave.

He is very calmly looking up at the rafters, guns drawn.

JOHNER
What if there's more? Let's stay here and let the army guys deal. Someone will come . . . I mean, where are the army guys?

CALL
They're dead.

Johner goes over to Wren, guns drawn. Distephano bravely steps in his way.

JOHNER
Then I don't think we need this asshole anymore . . .

DISTEPHANO
Step back—

CALL
(to Johner)
Stop it!

JOHNER
(turning to Call)
You got no authority here, you're a fucking mole.

CALL
We're not killing anybody! Nobody we don't have to.

CHRISTIE
Doctor. That thing, that's your pet goddamn project?

WREN
Yes.

CHRISTIE
And there're others. How many?

The doctor looks around, almost guiltily.

WREN
Twenty.

JOHNER
Twenty! We're fucked in our pink bottoms if there's
twenty of those things.

RIPLEY
There'll be more.

*Everyone looks around at her. She's squatting in the corner, facing
away from them.*

RIPLEY
They'll breed. In a few hours there'll be twice that number.
(she stands, approaches)
So who do I have to fuck to get off this boat?

They look at her, uncertainly. She makes them kind of nervous.

JOHNER
Wait a second here . . .

CALL
She is the host. Wren cloned her 'cause she had one of
those inside her.

CHRISTIE
That explains a lot.

CALL
She's a risk. Leave her.

JOHNER
I gotta go with Call on this one.

                         CHRISTIE
She comes.

                         CALL
She's not human! She's part of his experiment and could
turn on us in a second!

                         CHRISTIE
I don't give a syphilitic fuck whether you people can get
along or not. If we've got a wish to live then we work
together. All of us.
                         (to Wren)
We all get off this boat. After that, it's every man for his
lonesome self.

                         WREN
All right. Thank you.

Call stands by Christie, eyes locked on Ripley.

                         CALL
You can't trust her.

                         CHRISTIE
I don't trust anyone.

SEQ. 49—INT. CORRIDOR/CELLBLOCK—A BIT LATER

*The group makes its way toward the cellblock, led by Christie and
Wren. Hillard is grieving, very quiet.*

*Call tries to put her hand on Hillard's shoulder, but Hillard
shrugs it off, staring at her.*

*Ripley, bringing up the rear, watches the whole group with a sort of
fascinated detachment. Call looks back at her. Ripley smiles coldly.*

ANGLE: IN THE CELLBLOCK

The group makes their way slowly, quietly. They pass Ripley's cell, the door smashed in. But the hall is empty now. Call is near Ripley, looking at her still.

CALL
I didn't think you'd do it.

RIPLEY
Do what?

CALL
Kill one of them. You don't . . . you don't hate them.
You don't give a shit about us. But you killed it.

RIPLEY
It was in my way.

CALL
And what happens if *we* get in your way?

RIPLEY
Is that something you think you're likely to do?

They approach a bank of elevators, but Wren points down an adjoining hallway. They are about to go there when the elevator door lights up, indicating arrival.

The group backs up, spreads out. Those who can find cover take it, guns drawn.

The elevator doors open. It is too dark inside to see. Suddenly sparks fly from the broken overhead in the elevator and a figure appears in the light. Everyone jolts, about to fire, before they realize it is:

Vriess, who sits in his chair, a shotgun in each hand, eyes wide. Even twitchier than they.

                    JOHNER
Oh, man . . .

                    CALL
Vriess!

                    VRIESS
                (mock casual)
Hey, whatchyou guys doing?

                    WREN
                (suspiciously)
Where were you?

                    VRIESS
I was in maintenance, snagging some parts. Then I had
a little visit.

                    JOHNER
Doc's got a bug up his ass 'cause Call's a mole and he
thinks we're a conspiracy.

                    VRIESS
                (looking at Call)
She's a what?

                    JOHNER
A spy. Came here with a big ass mission to stop the
military from breeding those things.

Call looks over at Vriess, uncertain. To her surprise, he smiles warmly.

> VRIESS
> Well, I can't exactly argue with that sentiment.

> CHRISTIE
> We've got a mission here, people. We wanna be moving.

> JOHNER
> What if we get to the *Betty* and they're all over it?

> WREN
> There's no reason to suppose they'd head there—

> RIPLEY
> They won't.

Everybody looks at her.

> RIPLEY
> They're breeding. They've got new bodies to work on.
> They'll stay close. If they send anybody out, it'll be here.
> Where the . . . meat is.

> CALL
> "The meat." Jesus.

> JOHNER
> Well, if we want to make decent time, I say we ditch the
> cripple.
> (to Vriess)
> No offense.

VRIESS
(giving him the finger)
None taken.

HILLARD
Nobody's left behind, Johner. Not even you.

Her voice is quiet, grief still thick in it. Nobody backtalks her.

CHRISTIE
So what's our route?

DISTEPHANO
(to Wren)
Sir? The lift shaft. The one above mess.

Wren nods, and Distephano turns to the others.

DISTEPHANO
Maintenance lifts. They run straight from the top of the
ship down to the kitchen. No stops, but if we can get in
the shaft, there's an access tunnel that runs right to the
dock.

CHRISTIE
Sounds reasonable.

DISTEPHANO
I don't have the code for the access tunnel door.

WREN
I can override.

DISTEPHANO
(indicating the route)
We'll go through the labs. Then down to mess.

ANGLE: VRIESS—

Is unloading additional ammo from inside his chair. He tosses one of his shotguns to Hillard.

VRIESS
They never check the chair . . .

He pulls out a grenade launcher. It's so compact it's almost cute, cradled one-handed like an Uzi.

VRIESS
Call.

She looks around and he tosses it to her.

JOHNER
How come she gets a piece?

CHRISTIE
If we're clear then let's get on it. We'll go by twos—

RIPLEY
We're moving.

CHRISTIE
What?

RIPLEY
The ship is moving. I can feel it.

VRIESS

This ship has stealthrun, even if we were moving there's
no way she could feel it—

WREN

No, she's right.

DISTEPHANO

If the ship suffers any serious damage, it autopilots back
to homebase.

HILLARD

What's homebase?

WREN

Earth.

CALL

Oh, God. Oh, you bastard . . .

JOHNER

Earth? I don't wanna go to that shithole.

CALL

If those things get to Earth, it'll be . . .

RIPLEY
(not very concerned)

The end.

CALL

We've got to blow the ship.

CHRISTIE

We don't have to do anything except get off it. How long till we get there?

DISTEPHANO
(looking at the screen)

Three hours. Almost.

CHRISTIE

Then that's what we've got. Let's move.

CALL

Don't you get it? This thing is gonna put down in the middle of a heavily populated quarantine base. No one'll have the slightest idea what's coming. We're gonna be rolling out the red carpet for the end of our species.

HILLARD

That's not our problem.

CHRISTIE

Call, you're not blowing this ship. Not while we're on it. Once we get clear, you do as you please.

CALL

There's not enough time—

CHRISTIE

Then we'd best hurry.
(to Ripley)
What are you called, *Ripley*? You mind taking the point?

She moves to the head of the line, and they start.

JOHNER
Earth, man . . . what a slum.

SEQ. 50—INT. LABS—LATER

As they progress, everyone with a gun has it at the ready. Ripley is a few yards in front. She stops, sniffs. Listens.

RIPLEY
Clear.

Johner moves up next to her.

JOHNER
You've come up against these things before?

RIPLEY
Yes.

JOHNER
So what'd you do?

RIPLEY
I died.

He lags behind a bit, thrown.

JOHNER
That wasn't really what I wanted to hear . . .

Distephano points to a door.

DISTEPHANO
This way.

And Ripley leads them in.

SEQ. 51—INT. LAB—CONTINUOUS

As Ripley enters, we can see that this lab has been trashed.

Ripley surveys the wreckage calmly, keeps moving. As the others file in, their horrified expressions lend contrast to her lack of one.

Johner finds a dead body in a cryotube. He slides the lid down to reveal a gaping chest wound.

> JOHNER
> Fuck me . . .

> CHRISTIE
> Let's keep moving.

The door to the next chamber is ajar. Christie and Vriess step in, then Ripley.

SEQ. 52—INT. NEXT CHAMBER

Christie nudges an overhead fluorescent with his gun. It has been broken, and swings, splashing the room intermittently with light.

ANGLE: A FACE—

Appears for a split second in the light—terrified.

Ripley turns, and he leaps at Ripley from out of the shadows. A metal bar slams into her side, throwing her off balance.

Christie spins, weapons up, and almost shoots the figure cowering in the corner. Everyone else rushes in as he swings the bar before him, eyes wild with terror.

PURVIS
Get away from me!

CHRISTIE
Drop the rod, man. Do it!

PURVIS
(wild with terror)
Get away . . .

But the energy is out of him. The rod falls with a hollow clatter. He looks weakly from face to face.

PURVIS
What's going on?

Vriess looks at his name, stitched on his coveralls.

VRIESS
Purvis, what's going on is that we're getting the fuck off this ghost ship.

PURVIS
What ship? Where am I? I was in cryo on the way to Xarem, work crew for the nickel refinery . . . I wake up, I don't understand . . . I saw something . . . horrible.

CALL
Look, you come with us. It's dangerous here.

Ripley sniffs. Cocks her head.

RIPLEY
Leave him.

CALL

Fuck you. We're not leaving anyone on this boat.

RIPLEY

He's carrying.

JOHNER

He's what?

RIPLEY

He's got one of them inside him. I can smell it.

PURVIS

Inside me? What?

JOHNER

Shit, I don't want one of those things birthing anywhere near my ass.

VRIESS

It's a bad risk.

CALL

We can't just leave him.

VRIESS

I thought you came here to stop them from spreading.

CALL
(to Wren, torn)
Isn't there a process, can't you stop it?

CHRISTIE
We've got no time for that.

WREN
I couldn't do it here. The lab's torn apart.

CHRISTIE
(quietly)
I could do him. Painless, back of the head. Might be the
best way.

CALL
There's gotta be another way. If we freeze him—

PURVIS
What's in-fucking-side me?!!

They all look at him, a bit sheepishly.

WREN
A parasite. A foreign element that—

Ripley steps in front of the doctor.

RIPLEY
There's a monster in your chest. They—
(indicating crew)
—hijacked your ship and sold your cryotube to him—
(indicating Wren)
—and he put an alien in you. In a few hours it'll punch
its way through your ribcage and you'll die. Any
questions?

Purvis is wide-eyed, stunned. After a moment he stammers:

PURVIS
Who are you?

RIPLEY
I'm the monster's mother.

She starts heading out of the chamber. Call turns to the others.

CALL
He comes with us. We can freeze him on the *Betty* and
the doctor can remove it later.

WREN
All right.

JOHNER
Since when are you in fucking charge?

CALL
Since you were born without balls.

VRIESS
Ease off, people.

CHRISTIE
(to Purvis, herding him along)
Come with us. You might even live. Get twitchy on me
and you will be shot.

They move out.

SEQ. 53—EXT. *AURIGA*

Gliding through space, passing the moons of Jupiter with dazzling speed.

SEQ. 54—INT. CORRIDOR—LATER

Ripley and Call are on point. Ripley looks down the hall.

Ripley stops dead, staring at a door.

CLONING STORAGE FACILITY is written on it. Stenciled beneath that is "1–7". Ripley stares. Tries the door, which opens.

> DISTEPHANO
> That's not the way.

> CHRISTIE
> Ripley, we got no time for sight-seeing.

Ripley is looking down at her arm, at the eight tattooed on it. She looks at Call. Looks back at Wren.

> WREN
> Ripley . . . don't.

She enters.

SEQ. 55—INT. CLONING STORAGE FACILITY—CONTINUOUS

She stands a moment, staring, before proceeding through it. Call stands in the doorway, the others crowding behind her. Every face registers the horror of what they are seeing, but none more so than Ripley's.

Numbers one through seven. The first failed efforts to clone Ripley.

They are lined up like museum exhibits—or side show freaks. Here is the fetal Ripley, the fetal alien visible through its translucent chest. In a jar. Here is a prematurely old, diseased Ripley, withered blue skin clinging to collapsed bones.

Here is an attempt to separate the alien and grow it without the host—boneless, bubbling tissue, a weak and useless mouth rigored in mid-mew. Each one more horrifying than the last, and the last the worst of all.

Ripley approaches, and stares at number seven.

A complete mixture of alien and human DNA. A tortured, disgusting hybrid, half Ripley, half nightmare.

Hooked up to wires and machines, it lies on the tilted table, its head nearly level with Ripley's as she finally approaches it.

When it opens its eyes, they are hers.

It turns its head ever so slightly to look at her. Recognizes her.

Ripley cannot even speak. She begins to shake slightly, looking at number seven.

> NUMBER SEVEN
> Kill . . . me . . .

Ripley's eyes go saucered as it speaks—speaks out of nothing resembling a mouth. Ripley staggers back a step, shaking badly now. This is too much to bear.

> CALL
> Ripley!

Ripley turns, slowly, still in a fever dream.

Call cocks the grenade launcher with a loud ch-chack. Her eyes meet Ripley's.

Call tosses it to Ripley as the crew steps back and even as she catches it, Ripley fires, a grenade chugging to the end of the room and bursting in fire and noise, she fires another, glass and steel exploding into flame, she turns to number seven, her hand shakes momentarily . . .

And she fires, the poor creature dissolving in a cloud of flame.

Freezing gas jets fill the room, extinguishing potential spread, but he heart of the firestorm continues to rage in the chamber.

She backs out, the crew waiting for her outside.

The launcher falls loudly to the ground. Ripley turns to Wren, her face rigid with pain. Wren backs up a step, looking around him for protection that the others have no thought of providing.

> CALL
> Ripley . . . Don't do it.

Ripley stops. Weariness suffusing her expression.

> RIPLEY
> Don't do what?

The tension passes. Wren breathes a sigh of relief.

Call punches him across the jaw, his head whipping around as he collapses to the ground. Call starts down the hall, not even looking at him.

> CALL
> Don't do that.

Wren feels his jaw, smiling at the absurdity of it all. It's kind of winning. Christie helps him up.

CHRISTIE

Had it coming, Doc.

Johner looks in at the burning lab.

JOHNER

What's the big deal? Fucking waste of ammo.

PURVIS

Let's get going before anything comes to check out the
noise.

JOHNER

Must be a chick thing.

SEQ. 56—INT. SHAFT

ANGLE: DISTEPHANO—

Opening a floor hatch.

DISTEPHANO

We go down from here.

CHRISTIE
(to Vriess)
We got to lose the chair, Vriess.

VRIESS

I know.

CHRISTIE

Kawlang maneuver, all right?

Vriess is pulling a coil of cords from the chair.

> VRIESS
> Just like old times . . .

SEQ. 57—INT. COOLING TOWER

Call drops down into the room from a ladder. Distephano and Johner are already down here, guns ready. They motion for Call to move on ahead, as more come down. Call procedes to the end of the room, where Ripley is.

CAMERA DOLLIES OUT, PRECEDING CALL—

Ripley is alert and ready—but it's clear she's far from over the pain of seeing the other clones. Her eyes are red, a little too wide, and as she holds her hands in front of her, they still shake badly.

Call stops next to her, awkwardly.

> CALL
> Anything?

Ripley shakes her head.

> CALL
> That lab . . . I can't imagine how that must feel.

Ripley giggles inanely, then chokes the giggle off before it can bloom into a scream. She looks back at Call.

> RIPLEY
> No. You can't.

She stops, feeling in her mouth with her tongue. Something bothers her.

CALL
What is it?

RIPLEY
Lost a tooth.

CALL
So?

RIPLEY
Got it back.

She feels the new tooth with her thumb. Perplexed.

ANGLE: THE CREW—

As they file silently along the room.

Bringing up the rear is Christie, toting a shotgun. He turns slowly, alert, and we see that Vriess is strapped to his back—facing the other way, also with a shotgun.

Ripley looks down. The floor here is covered with a foot or so of dark water. She steps into it, moves up a few paces. The others gingerly follow. Vriess is facing the back. He looks up.

VRIESS
It's the cooling tanks. Somebody must have opened the valve.

ANGLE: THE COOLING TANKS

We see the liquid pouring out from the openings.

JOHNER
The nasties couldn't have done it, could they?

                       HILLARD
What for . . . ?

They continue moving slowly through the water, looking about them.

ANGLE: LEGS—

Sunk in black water up to the thigh. Extremely vulnerable.

                      WREN
Down here.

                    JOHNER
                (not pleased)
As in 'down'? As in 'swim'?

The water here is waist deep. Wren looks down at a stairwell, just the top of the railing visible above the murky water.

                    WREN
We're at the bottom of the ship. There's no other way.
It's just through the kitchen, then up the elevator shaft.
Maybe seventy feet from here.

                  CHRISTIE
                (to Vriess)
You ready to get wet, partner?

                  VRIESS
Oh yeah.

                  HILLARD
You sure about the distance?

                    WREN
Yes.

                    JOHNER
Hold it. Is anybody else noticing that this sucks?

                    CALL
Why don't we send out a scout? So we're not flying
blind.

                    WREN
It's not a bad idea.

                    DISTEPHANO
I'll go, sir.

                    CHRISTIE
I think Ripley's our man. Feel like making yourself
useful?

                    RIPLEY
                (smiling grimly)
I'm just happy to be here.

She takes a couple of big breaths—

                    WREN
Just go straight. You'll see it.

And she plunges under.

*The others wait. The tanks are almost empty now, no more water
running through the valves. Silence falls. No one moves.*

ANGLE: DISTEPHANO

He flips caps over the barrel of the gun, slides a panel over the digital readout. The burner is ready to go, watertight. He looks over at Christie's weapon.

                    DISTEPHANO
You should do like me.

                    CHRISTIE
These are disposables. They can take it.

                    DISTEPHANO
Disposables, huh? I heard about those. How many rounds?

                    CHRISTIE
Twenty. Split points, give you a good hole even at the smaller caliber.

                    DISTEPHANO
Cool.

                    CHRISTIE
They're big with hitters.

                    DISTEPHANO
Hitters?
                    (gets it)
Oh.

                    CHRISTIE
Cause you throw 'em away after the kill. Nobody likes to throw away a weapon they're attached to. You know.

Distephano is obviously made uncomfortable by the turn the conversation has taken.

HILLARD
I think you've frightened soldier boy.

DISTEPHANO
No, it's just . . . you're pretty casual about killing.

CHRISTIE
We were talking guns. What do you use them for, to teach Sunday school?

HILLARD
At least our pieces can put those aliens down. A lot faster than that Easy-Bake crap you're carrying.

ANGLE: VRIESS—

Watching the ceiling.

ANGLE: CALL—

Splashes water on her face. Looks around, starting to worry a bit.

CALL
Taking her time . . .

Suddenly, bubbles come to the surface. The crew tenses up, waiting. After a while, the bubbles stop.

And Ripley shoots up to the surface in the foreground. Everyone jumps.

WREN
Are we good?

RIPLEY

We're okay. Door was stuck about twenty yards in. I got it open. I didn't go all the way through but it lays out just like you said. Shouldn't be a problem to make it to the shaft.

CHRISTIE

Let's do it, then.

CALL

Do I have to tell everyone to take a deep breath?

A couple of the guys smile.

One by one the entire crew slips down into the black water.

SEQ. 58—INT. STAIRWELL/KITCHEN—CONTINUOUS

It's all underwater. Visibility is poor. The crew move swiftly and gracefully down the stairs and into the ktichen.

In here it's a tad labyrithian, and the size of the room makes it darker. Wren heads straight for the other end.

They swim. Safety is a good fifty feet away.

They are tense, concentrated. Swimming past dark spaces. Anything could be hiding here.

Johner looks about him, very nervous. Dark spaces. He looks behind him.

Three aliens are right behind him.

Panic blows half the air out of his mouth as he swings around and fires at them, tags one as the other two swim off into the shadows with horrible ease.

Ripley, all the way to the stairs, sees. She hurries the others past her.

They swim frantically for safety, Hillard, Wren, Christie, and Vriess—Johner bringing up the rear, still firing at the third one, wounding it but not scoring the killshot.

Call is swimming up the staircase, the growing light above indicating the surface. She is almost to it when she is caught in the web.

A net of translucent alien goo is spread just six inches below the surface. Call struggles, the goo sticking to her, she's running out of air—as Wren and Christie encounter the same thing—they all try to tear through it, but they are getting weaker—

Ripley looks back as the last of the crew is passing her, the aliens close behind. She looks up to see the situation above and quickly makes for the surface—but an alien grabs her foot, holding her down—now she is running out of air—she kicks at it, it lets go—

The others are fighting, Call pops her stiletto and cuts through the web, but it's tough, she still can't get her head up.

Distephano, off to the side, is drowning. He takes in a huge mouthful of water and begins thrashing.

Hillard is firing wildly—an alien grabs her head, pulls her into the darkness.

Ripley swims past everyone and grabs the hole Call cut, pulls it apart with a mighty heave, she glides up through—

CLOSE UP: RIPLEY'S FACE—

Just breaks the surface, she takes in a huge gasp of air, and a face-hugger clamps down on her.

Ripley goes back under, pulling at the thing as others break the surface.

Wren comes up, looks around. Eggs have been placed all around the surface of the water. He barely has time to take this in before two more open.

A face-hugger springs out of one, leaps right at him—but Call nails it in two shots.

Christie and Vriess break surface, still strapped together. They both begin firing, back to back, in a circular sweep. They create a circle of fire as they spin, bullets blasting out of both their weapons. They decimate a number of eggs.

ANGLE: UNDERWATER

Ripley pulls the face-hugger with all her might—it comes off, its fingers singeing the sides of her face, leaving marks like warpaint. Worse, its probing fleshy member pulls last out of her throat, thrashing horribly.

In utmost disgust, Ripley pulls it apart. Looks around and the three aliens are coming right at her.

ANGLE: ABOVE THE SURFACE

Most of the crew has gotten up out of the water. Christie is holding a face-hugger inches from his face, others screaming, taking a bead on it.

Christie wrenches it off him, hurling it away. Johner nails it in midflight.

Johner pulls Distephano out of the water, but he is not breathing.

Ripley comes up out of the water, and an alien rises right behind her. Everyone who can, shoots it. It falls back into the water.

CHRISTIE
A trap! They set a goddamn ambush!

JOHNER
Give me that!

He pulls the burner off Distephano's body even as Call is giving him mouth to mouth.

Johner flips the gun open and fires at the water, the whole thing smoking and sizzling with the electrical charge. We hear an alien wail bubble from below the surface.

> JOHNER
> (grinning feverishly)
> Okay! Everybody out of the pool!

> VRIESS
> Let's *get*!

Distephano sputters back to life. Ripley picks him up with one hand.

SEQ. 59—INT. SHAFT

The shaft goes up about four stories. Enough room for three elevators.

> WREN
> Up!

He starts climbing. It's not that hard—there are ladders in each shaft section. Call comes up behind him. Ripley and others pair off on other ladders.

ANGLE: LEDGE

Wren comes to a crawlspace ledge. He climbs on. Set back a few feet from the shaft is a small maintenance access door. He works the keypad beside it as Call climbs up behind him.

The aliens smash through the door, one of them sailing across the shaft to grab a pipe on the other side. Instantly four of them are swarming up the walls, moving much faster on pipes and ridges than the humans on ladders.

A face-hugger crawls on one of the aliens, constantly moving about on the adult alien's head like a frightened spider.

> CALL
> Hurry!

> WREN
> It's jammed! Shit! Gun!

She hands him her gun and without hesitation he shoots her through the chest.

She flies back and down the shaft, lands hard on the elevator six stories below. Eyes wide and empty.

ANGLE: RIPLEY—

Shocked. And surprised she's shocked.

> VRIESS
> NOO!!

He fires up at Wren, but Wren has punched in the code and slipped through the opening door.

Ripley leaps through the air and grabs the ledge, hauling herself up just in time to see the door shut.

The lock lights turn red. She slams against the door, but to no avail.

Ripley is shaking, abandoning herself to her fury. Suddenly an alien rises over the ledge. It's not three feet away from her and she screams, hurls herself at it and they both go flying off into space. They hit the wall on the other side, they fall. Ripley grabs a pole, it practically tears her arm out of its socket but she holds on. The alien isn't so lucky, it plummets, unable to find purchase.

We see it fall past the unmoving body of Call.

ANGLE: CALL'S FACE—

As the face-hugger clamps onto it. Pauses. Pushes off a bit, two digits probing Call's nostrils.

Sensing no breath, the things scurries away to find a better host.

ANGLE: JOHNER

He is firing down at the aliens. Looks up and screams.

ANGLE: JOHNER'S POV

There's a spider on the wall right in front of him. Unhesitatingly, he shoots the shit out of it.

Another alien is fast approaching Christie and Vriess. Vriess frantically tries to reload.

> VRIESS
> It's on us!

> CHRISTIE
> Switch!

Christie turns, aims—Vriess grabs the ladder as Christie fires, but the alien is too close, it grabs Christie, spurting blood all over him. He screams, fires again. The alien has him in its grasp, though.

He flicks open his switchblade and slices through the bonds holding him to Vriess.

> VRIESS
> What are you— Christie!

Christie falls, taking the alien with him. Vriess continues up, crying.

ANGLE: THE DOOR

Lights come on, indicating it's about to open. They train their guns on it.

It opens to reveal Call, dripping wet but not particularly dead.

>   CALL
> Come on.

SEQ. 60—INT. HALL—SECONDS LATER

They pile out of the shaft. They all breathe hard, exhausted, before they can muster for the next stretch. Call stands with her back to them.

>   RIPLEY
> Where's Wren?

>   CALL
> Long gone. I found an air duct, worked my way up.

>   VRIESS
> Man, am I glad to see you. Are you hurt?

>   CALL
> I'm fine.

>   DISTEPHANO
> You got body armor on?

>   CALL
> Yeah. Come on.

Ripley isn't buying.

RIPLEY
You took it in the chest. I saw.

CALL
I'm fine!

Ripley spins her around. Call stares at Ripley sullenly. A small trickle of metallic blue fluid trickles down from the corner of her eye. Ripley looks down.

ANGLE: CALL'S CHEST

Wren has indeed made a messy hole here, got her right in the chest, but where there should be blood and bone, there is a tangle of synth-organic wiring.

RIPLEY
A robot.

JOHNER
Son of a bitch. Little Annalee's just full of surprises.

RIPLEY
(quietly)
I should have known. All that crap about being human—there's no one so zealous as a Born Again.

JOHNER
I thought synthetics were supposed to be all logical and shit. She's a big ol' psycho!

VRIESS
(to Call)
You're a Second Gen, aren't you?

                              CALL
          Leave me alone.

*Her voice shocks her more than anyone—her vocal track slips, affected
by the wounds. The voice is a shade slow, and echoes strangely.*

                              VRIESS
          Call . . .

                              CALL
                            (bitterly)
          Yes.

                              JOHNER
          Second Gen? Shit.

                           DISTEPHANO
                           (to Ripley)
          Autons. Robots designed by robots. Highly ethical and
          emotional, with complex paradigmatic reasoning
          structures. They were supposed to revitalize the
          synthetic industry. Instead they buried it.

Ripley looks at the girl.

                              RIPLEY
          They were too good.

                           DISTEPHANO
          Oh yeah. Overrode their own behavioral inhibitors.
          Didn't like being told what to do. The government
          ordered a recall. Fucking massacre.

VRIESS
I always heard there were a few that got out intact, but
man . . . I never thought I'd see one.

PURVIS
(getting anxious)
It's great, she's a toaster oven . . . Can we leave now?

RIPLEY
How much time till we land?

DISTEPHANO
Under two hours.

*Vriess looks at Call's wound. Amid the dark blue mess, a host of
black insectile threads are automatically repairing the damage
inside.*

VRIESS
Jesus . . .

*He can't conceal his disgust, seeing it. Call pulls away. Ripley
watches them, senses the new dynamic in the group: Call is outside,
an unknown—not unlike Ripley herself.*

JOHNER
Yeah, get your socket wrench, Vriess. Maybe she just
needs an oil change. Can't believe I almost fucked that
thing.

VRIESS
Yeah, like you've never fucked a robot.

They start off again.

ANGLE: RIPLEY—

Letting Distephano lead.

> DISTEPHANO
>
> Shit.

They have reached an access door. Debris blocks the way.

> RIPLEY
>
> Another way?

> DISTEPHANO
>
> Through the wall. We'll have to get one of these panels off.

> RIPLEY
>
> What about Wren? If he gets in the computer he can really dick us around.

> JOHNER
>
> We have to get in too.

> DISTEPHANO
>
> There's no access console on this level. And I don't have the security access that Wren does anyway.

Ripley turns to Call. The girl is still somewhat apart from the group.

> RIPLEY
>
> Call.

> CALL
>
> No. I can't.

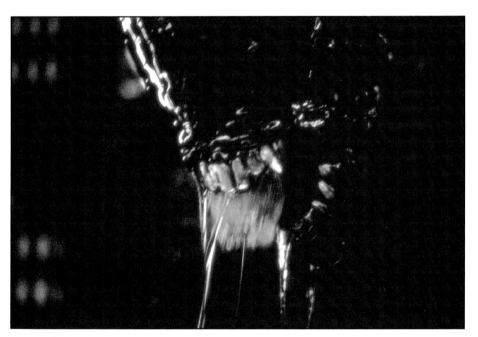

ALIEN WARRIOR

RIPLEY (SIGOURNEY WEAVER)

CALL (WINONA RYDER)

THE SCIENTISTS

VRIESS (DOMINIQUE PINON) AND A GUARD

CHRISTIE (GARY DOURDON)

JOHNER (RON PERLMAN) JERRYRIGGING CABLE

READY FOR ACTION

CHRISTIE CLIMBING LADDER, VRIESS ON HIS BACK

THROUGH THE FLOODED SECTIONS

ALIEN NEST

The Alien Queen

JOHNER
Bullshit. She damn well talkie machinie.

VRIESS
Any of the new model droids can access the mainframe.
Just by blinking.

CALL
I can't.
(off their looks)
I *can't*. I burned my wave modem. We all did.

VRIESS
You can still patch in manually.

*Call looks over at the group, staring at her with varying degrees of
contempt. She knows she doesn't have a choice.*

DISTEPHANO
There's ports in the chapel.

RIPLEY
Come on.
(to the others)
You, get started on that wall.

SEQ. 61—INT. CHAPEL—CONTINUOUS

*Ripley and Call enter the small room. It is a classic chapel, just a
little cleaner and a lot smaller.*

*Behind the altar, a small stained glass "window" is bolted to the
wall, lit by pinlights.*

*Call stands between the pew and reflexively crosses herself. Ripley
gives her a look.*

RIPLEY
You programmed for that?

Ripley sits in one of the pews, pulls out a Bible. It somewhat resembles a Newton. Under the leather flap is a screen reading: HOLY BIBLE. PRESS START.

Ripley pulls out the cord from the Bible's port, holds it up.

CALL
Don't make me do this.

RIPLEY
Don't make me make you.

CALL
I don't want to go in there.

RIPLEY
Get over it.

CALL
It's like . . . your insides are liquid. It's not real.

RIPLEY
You can blow the ship. Before it reaches Earth. Kill them all. Just give us time to get out first.

That convinces Call. She pulls up her sleeve and begins. She pushes a part of her forearm, just below the crook of her elbow.

It has a spring release catch, and a small panel rises with two computer ports on it. She takes the cable from Ripley and plugs it in. It looks almost like she's mainlining heroin.

She cocks her head.

CALL

Damnit.

RIPLEY

Anything?

CALL

Hold on.

She reaches in her chest, reconnects some tubes. She twitches, then her eyes suddenly dilate massively.

It's beginning.

She begins speaking very rapidly.

CALL

Breach in sector seven, sector three—sector nine unstable—engines operating at eighty-six percent—forty-six minutes until Earthdock.

Her voice has a mechanical quality as she rattles this off.

She stops, returns somewhat to herself.

CALL

We burned too much energy—I can't make critical mass. I can't blow it.

RIPLEY

Then crash it.

SEQ. 62—INT. CORRIDOR—CONTINUOUS

The crew works at getting the wall panel off.

Purvis is helping pry open a corner. He grimaces, beads of sweat popping out on his forehead. Suddenly he lets go, clutching his chest.

The others stop, look at him. Johner and Distephano bring up their weapons warily.

Purvis grits his teeth, waits it out. Looks up at the others as the pain passes.

> PURVIS
> I'm okay. I'm okay. Really. I feel good.

One eye still on him, they get back to work.

SEQ. 63—INT. CHAPEL—A BIT LATER

> CALL
> Ground level recalibrated . . . new destination 760, 403. Uninhabited quadrant. Braking systems off-line, acceleration increase—time until impact now forty-three minutes, eight seconds.

> RIPLEY
> Try to clear us a path to the ship. And start her up.

Call closes her eyes and:

ANGLE: A DOOR—

In a corridor opens, then another, then a third opening to the antechamber, the last room before the loading dock. And—

ANGLE: THE *BETTY'S* COCKPIT

We see the ship switch on, hear the humming of the engine.

SEQ. 64—INT. CHAPEL

CALL
Ship in prep, fuel on line . . .
(her brow creases)
Tracking movement in sublevels six through nine.
Video is down. Attempted rerouting nonfunctional,
wait, partial visual in Waste Tank Five, unauthorized
presence . . .

RIPLEY
Unauthorized?

CALL
Non-human.

RIPLEY
How many?

CALL
Please wait . . . emergency override in console 45V, level
one . . . handprint ID . . .
(like herself)
It's Wren. He's almost at the *Betty*.

RIPLEY
(imitating Wren)
And how do you feel about that?

SEQ. 65—INT. CORRIDOR—CONTINUOUS

Wren is holding his hand to the scanner, just as Call described.

The red light turns green and the locks in the door clack open.

>   FATHER
Emergency override validated.

The door begins to rise. Looking around him, Wren waits to go through.

The door grinds to a halt, still too low to climb under. The lights go out, only the faintest glow coming from the various instrument panels. Wren's expression drains.

>   WREN
Father, reboot systems on 45V, authorization "starling."

Nothing happens. Wren looks about him, beginning to sweat. Did the aliens do this?

>   WREN
Father, locate power drain, report. Father?

>   CALL
(on the system)
Father's dead, asshole.

Wren spins in shock at the sound of Call's voice. It's everywhere around him.

ANGLE: THE CONSOLE

We see a reading: SUBSTITUTE VOICE MATRIX ACCEPTED. Call isn't speaking over the P.A., she is the P.A.

ANGLE: THE DOOR—

Slams back down, locks click into place. The doors behind him open up, emergency lighting pulsing along toward him.

CALL/SHIP
Intruder on level one . . . all aliens please proceed to
level one.

*Wren is freaking. He runs back down the corridor, looking about
him wildly.*

SEQ. 66—INT. CHAPEL—CONTINUOUS

Call pulls the cord out of her port.

RIPLEY
You got a mean streak.

CALL
It's done. That should hold— Damnit—

*Her voice track slips again. She works the wires in her chest, trying
to fix it.*

RIPLEY
Let me see—

CALL
Don't touch me.

Ripley backs off.

CALL
You must think this is pretty funny.

RIPLEY
Yes. But I'm finding a lot of things funny lately. And I'm
not sure they are.

> CALL
Why do you go on living? How can you stand it? How can you stand . . . yourself?

Ripley shrugs.

> RIPLEY
Not much choice.

> CALL
At least there's a part of you that's human. I'm just . . . fuck. Look at me . . .

She looks at the hole in her chest, the blue and sticky fibers.

> CALL
I'm disgusting

Her voice is at its slowest here, low and eerie. It's a mechanical problem, but it sounds just like despair.

Ripley cannot help but feel some sympathy for the girl.

> RIPLEY
Why did you come here?

> CALL
To kill you, remember?
> (after a beat)
Before the "recall" I accessed the mainframe. Every dirty little covert op the government ever dreamed of is in there. And this. The aliens, you . . . even the connection with Elgyn and the *Betty*. And I knew if they succeeded, it would be the end of them.

As she says it, her voice has returned to normal.

RIPLEY
Why do you care what happens to them?

CALL
(bitterly)
Because I'm programmed to.

RIPLEY
Are you programmed to be such an asshole? Are you the
new asshole model they're putting out?

*This actually gets a smile from the desolate Call. When next she
speaks, there is a closeness in her tone that wasn't there before.*

CALL
I couldn't let them do it. I couldn't let them annihilate
themselves. Do you understand?

RIPLEY
I did, once. I tried to save . . . people . . . Didn't work
out. There was a girl. She had bad dreams. I tried to
help her and she died . . . and I can't remember her
name.

Call says nothing. For a moment, Ripley can't either.

Distephano enters.

DISTEPHANO
I guess we're almost there.

RIPLEY
Right.

He exits again. Call looks up at Ripley.

RIPLEY
Do you dream?

CALL
I . . . we have neural processors that run through . . .
(stops)
Yes.

RIPLEY
When I sleep, I dream about it. Them. Every night. All
around me . . . in me. I used to be afraid to dream, but
I'm not anymore.

CALL
Why?

RIPLEY
Because no matter how bad the dreams get . . . when I
wake up it's always worse.

*A moment, and then they quietly start out of the chapel. Call's
voice, now programmed permanently into the ship, calmly sounds
over the P.A.*

CALL/SHIP
Ventilation systems stabilized, oxygen at 43%.

CALL
Do I really sound like that?

SEQ. 67—EXT. SPACE

As the Auriga *speeds along.*

SEQ. 68—INT. CORRIDOR

As they are prying off the last sheet of metal in their way.

> DISTEPHANO
> Won't be far now.

> PURVIS
> God, I'm so tired . . .

> JOHNER
> Yeah, well, we'll sleep when we're dead.

Ripley appears next to him, Call behind her.

> RIPLEY
> Don't count on it.

Ripley hands Call Elgyn's shotgun. She moves to the front, grabs the sheet of metal and easily rips it out of the wall. Beyond is darkness. The crew shine lights in there to see:

ANGLE: NEXT HALL

An alien scape. Covered with smooth, dripping resin, it resembles a natural cavern more than a man-made craft. Though there is no movement, the alien presence is palpable. This is their homebase, or close to it.

Everyone stares.

> PURVIS
> Uh, this is bad, right?

> RIPLEY
> We must be near the nest.

VRIESS
Well, then we go another way.

DISTEPHANO
There isn't one. This is it.

JOHNER
No, okay, now, fuck you. 'Cause I ain't going in there.

CALL
Soldier's right. I did a diagnostic on the ship. Unless we go all the way back—

VRIESS
I can live with that— .

CALL
—which we don't have time for.

JOHNER
We got near ninety minutes.

CALL
Not any more.

DISTEPHANO
What are you saying?

JOHNER
What did you do, robot?

                    RIPLEY
Forget it.

                    JOHNER
Hey, you wanna die here with your little brothers and
sisters, that's fine. But I plan to live past today and if this
hunk of plastic is pulling some shit I'm gonna kill her.
                  (to Call)
Kill you. Does that fucking compute. Or do you want
me to . . .

*Ripley's hand shoots out and grabs Johner's tongue. He stops,
unable to speak.*

                    RIPLEY
It'd make a hell of a necklace . . .

*A moment, and she lets go. Johner knows better than to start up again.
Ripley turns to Distephano.*

                    RIPLEY
How far to the docks?

                  DISTEPHANO
Hundred yards.

They all look at the forbidding corridor.

                    VRIESS
So what's the plan?

SEQ. 69—INT. ALIEN CORRIDOR—MOMENTS LATER

*The crew is running really fast. That's the plan. They all look
shitscared, but nobody says a word. Johner has Vriess strapped to his
back and he's still making the best time of anyone.*

Ripley brings up the rear. She is disturbed, slightly overwhelmed by her surroundings. She looks about her constantly. So far, no movement.

She stops suddenly, clutching her head.

ANGLE: A WINDOW—

At the end of the hall—it looks down on the area leading to the docks, the floor of which is fifteen feet below. The crew, minus Ripley, arrive.

They look down at what appears to be relative safety.

Call steps forward with the shotgun and blasts the window. The noise echoes eerily in the corridor.

It seems to be answered by another noise. A kind of roar, coming from all around them.

Without a word they start climbing through the window, dropping down into the next chamber. Call looks around, notices for the first time:

                         CALL
        Where's Ripley?

Purvis is the last one left. He looks at Call. She motions for Purvis to go, then heads back for Ripley.

SEQ. 70—INT. ALIEN CORRIDOR—CONTINUOUS

Call finds Ripley staggering, nearly doubled over.

                         CALL
        Ripley! What's wrong?

Ripley doesn't even hear her; something else drowns Call out. Ripley puts her hands over her ears.

> RIPLEY
>
> Mistake . . . mistake . . .

> CALL
>
> Ripley.

> RIPLEY
>
> I can hear them . . . So close . . .

> CALL
>
> Jesus. Come on.

> RIPLEY
>
> I can hear them . . . The Queen . . .

> CALL
>
> What . . . ?

> RIPLEY
>
> She's in pain.

They crash up through the floor panels, six of them, surrounding Ripley.

Call barely has time to raise her gun before they drag Ripley down, and when she pulls the trigger it merely clicks, empty.

> CALL
>
> Ripley!

She dives, comes up to the edge of the hole in the floor paneling, trying to grab Ripley. She looks down—pulls out her light and shines it down the hole—and sees:

ANGLE: IN THE HOLE—

A nest of vipers. A swarm of black, insectile bodies, enveloping Ripley. The woman sinks as though in quicksand. Call just has time to see Ripley's face disappear.

CALL

NOOO!!!

SEQ. 71—INT. AIR VENT—CONTINUOUS

Dark, cramped, and already covered with a hardening layer of resin like the hall above.

Skittering, insectile motion at one end heralds the aliens, as two of them crawl rapidly along. The third crawls upside down, the semiconscious Ripley draped over its chest. It holds her almost gently.

Scuttling through a small maze, the aliens come out into:

SEQ. 72—INT. WASTE TANK FIVE—CONTINUOUS

A vast, dark chamber, entirely encrusted with alien goo. The air vent opens about three quarters of the way up the chamber. The aliens pour out and immediately scuttle up, carrying Ripley to the top of the chamber.

They circle her and begin secreting resin, spinning a web around her. The resin comes out of them in spits and globs. It isn't pleasant, and Ripley struggles feebly as they begin to cocoon her.

SEQ. 73—INT. ANTECHAMBER—CONTINUOUS

The crew piles through it on their way to the loading dock. Call brings up the rear, still looking back regretfully. She hesitates, and Purvis takes hold of her arm.

PURVIS
We got to be moving, Miss. Best gift you can give her right now is a quick death.

CALL
It's not right . . .

PURVIS
I've been saying that all day.

A moment more, and she heads out with him.

SEQ. 74—WASTE TANK FIVE—CONTINUOUS

The aliens have finished webbing Ripley, and climb away. When it is done she finds herself basically hung from the ceiling, her legs encased and glued with glistening strands to the wall. She hangs therefore at an angle, looking down on the chamber. And so it is with her, as she swims to full consciousness, that we get our first real look at where we are.

There are no less than ten people strung up exactly as Ripley is, encircling the chamber, and all looking some forty feet down at:

The Queen. Lying on her back at the bottom of the chamber, belly swollen and distended. She is herself partially cocooned, strapped down in the middle of a black pool of blood and ichor. Her head moves slowly back and forth, in a delirium of pain.

There are four or five aliens tending her, spinning goo around her, vomiting blood onto her belly. They might be serving her, or imprisoning her. Both, in fact.

There is one thing missing from this tableau.

RIPLEY
(softly)
No eggs . . .

GEDIMAN
(O.S.)
Our greatest achievement.

CAMERA SWINGS IN A PANNING MOVEMENT—

Ripley turns slowly, to see the person next to her. It's Gediman, looking wan and haggard.

He may be speaking to her, but he stares straight ahead, his eyes glowing with near insanity.

GEDIMAN
A secondary reproductive cycle. Asexual, mammalian . . .
no host.

RIPLEY
That's not possible.

GEDIMAN
We thought we could alter its reproductive system,
obviate the egg-laying cycle. But the beast doesn't trade.
It just added a second cycle. What a wonder.

A keening shriek comes out of the Queen, as her limbs begin thrashing. The aliens around her back off slightly, chattering their insectile hymn.

RIPLEY
But how . . .

GEDIMAN
Genetic crossover. From the host DNA. From the
human.

RIPLEY

No . . .

GEDIMAN

Look at it. It's you. It's you!

Ripley does look, barely fighting back tears of horror and frustration. Of despair.

The bulge in the Queen's belly starts moving.

Ripley starts struggling with her bonds, sudden determination in her eyes.

RIPLEY

I'm getting out of here. Goddamnit, I'm getting out of here.

Gediman looks at her, the last glimmer of his sanity sinking beyond the horizon.

GEDIMAN

Don't you want to see what happens next?

SEQ. 75—INT. LOADING DOCK—CONTINUOUS

The crew rushes in, heads for the Betty.

JOHNER

How long till we can get airborne?

VRIESS

I'll need Call to patch in to the ship again, open the hatch.

CALL
Right.

JOHNER
We hit atmo in a few minutes, only gonna make it harder.

They all run on board.

SEQ. 76—INT. *BETTY*

They head for the cockpit. Distephano deposits Vriess in another wheelchair.

CALL
Johner, take Purvis to the freezer.

JOHNER
All right. Nap time, buddy.

A gunshot—and Purvis goes flying, blood spurting out of his shoulder. Johner draws but Wren emerges from the shadows too fast.

Wren grabs Call and very carefully holds his gun to her back, right below the shoulder blade.

WREN
You move and I put a bullet where her brain is!

Johner stands, uncertain.

WREN
Distephano! Take their weapons.

DISTEPHANO
Begging your pardon, sir, but eat my fuck.

Distephano aims at Wren. Wren backs up a step.

WREN
Drop it! Drop it or we all die together!

Heaped in the corner, Purvis suddenly jerks forward. His eyes go wide.

SEQ. 77—INT. WASTE TANK FIVE—CONTINUOUS

Ripley is frantically trying to pull at her bonds. It's just beginning to work.

But the noise is getting worse, the aliens frantically agitated . . .

CAMERA DOLLIES FORWARD—

. . . as the Queen's belly begins moving more violently.

She shrieks, and Ripley does as well, from effort or sympathy, it's hard to tell.

The Queen's belly starts to open. It looks painful, blood seeping out around the belly. It's also horribly natural, an obscene mockery of human vaginal birth.

And the Newborn emerges.

An alien, to be sure, but nothing we've seen so far. It's bone white. Its head is long, eyeless, like the others, but along its white expanse run red veins, coming out of the skin and running like thick bloody hairs to the back. It's much bigger than the others, nearly the size of the Queen herself.

And there is something human about it. Maybe the stance, though its hind legs are huge. Or the noise, like a hissing laugh, as it comes upright. Maybe it's just the tilt of the head.

GEDIMAN
Beautiful . . . beautiful butterfly . . .

He is crying with revelatory joy. Ripley is not. Grimacing at the sight and smell of the new beast, she begins pulling again at her bonds.

The Queen moans, thrashing gently now, reaching for its quivering issue. The Newborn crawls up onto its mother, faces it.

It viciously rips the Queen's face off. The keening shriek of the collective brood becomes almost too much for Ripley as the Newborn tears right through his mother's flesh.

One of the soldiers, at the other end of the room from Ripley, wakes up.

Dangling uselessly at his side is a rifle—the real deal, not a burner.

SOLDIER
No, God ...

He screams in uncomprehending horror. The Newborn stops, tilts its head.

It crawls gracefully up the side of the tank. Comes to the screaming soldier, gripping his sides as he screams lustily.

It holds him a moment, then rips his scalp off, plunging its teeth into his brain. We watch it drain the blood from his body. Its external ventricles swell, red tinged, as the soldier's body goes blue and slack. His rifle drops into the black pool.

The Newborn finishes, withdraws.

Gediman giggles. It turns to him.

SEQ. 78—INT. *BETTY*—CONTINUOUS

Johner's gun drops to the floor. Everyone backs off.

> WREN
This synthetic bitch is going to plug back into the
Auriga and land it according to standard operational
procedure.

> CALL
No, she's not.

> DISTEPHANO
You're nuts. You still want to bring those things back to
Earth?

> VRIESS
Have you been paying any attention today?

*The suffering of Purvis, still on the floor, is getting more and more
intense.*

Wren is getting more and more nervous.

> WREN
The aliens will be contained by the base quarantine
troops.

> CALL
For about five seconds.

> WREN
Shut up!!!

*And Purvis launches from the corner, screaming, jumps on
Wren—Wren gets off a couple of shots—Distephano gets it in the
shoulder and drops his weapon, spinning and falling—the other
shots hit the ship.*

Call dives for cover as Purvis slams his fist across Wren's face. Wren fires again and Johner is on the ground, rolling, grabbing his gun—

Purvis is a man possessed. He graps Wren's gunhand and smashes it against an instrument panel, bone cracking audibly as Wren drops the gun.

Purvis jerks. Blood blooms in his chest.

Everybody stops, mesmerized. Wren drops to his knees, going for the gun, and Purvis grabs him from behind, pulls him, pins him so that the back of Wren's head is against his chest.

Purvis jerks again. It takes Wren a moment to understand what's happening.

They both scream.

The alien bursts out of Purvis's chest, straight into Wren's skull.

Everyone else is still frozen. Then the little critter bursts out of Wren's face, flying straight at Vriess.

SEQ. 79—INT. WASTE TANK FIVE—CONTINUOUS

Ripley tears one of her arms free as the Newborn feeds beside her. Gediman is already a shell. Still working on the scientist, it turns to her. It has no eyes, but she can feel them on her anyway. It hisses that near-laugh.

Finishing, it makes to jump over to Ripley.

It regards her a moment, looks her up and down. She shakes slightly.

It extends a tongue unlike any we've seen before—ridged and metallic seeming like the others, but flexible. Writhing with a will of its own. Instead of killing Ripley, it starts licking at the webbing that holds her head, gently freeing her.

Ripley stares in near shock as it frees her arm, bringing itself closer to her. Something like a sigh escapes it.

Ripley reaches out and tentatively puts her hand on its smooth head, runs it gently along it. It turns its head and she can see a filmy, reptilian eye open and regard her.

The Newborn wraps its arms around her. She is trying hard not to shake. She looks down as it presses itself against her . . . a slit in its belly moves, widens as a dripping protuberance begins to emerge. It looks mostly like a giant earwig. But it's not. Ripley gasps audibly as the creature's intentions become clear.

She pushes it away with a sudden jerk—pulls at her remaining bonds with a terrible effort—she pulls free with a scream, plunging the thirty feet into the pool.

Ripley disappears beneath the surface of the gunk.

The Newborn turns its head, hissing with fury, trying to locate her. Other aliens scuttle closer to the pool.

Ripley stands up out of the pool, covered in blood, hoisting the soldier's gun. Kill-shriek rising from her throat as she fires, taking out a host of aliens in a single sweep, just tagging the Newborn as it leaps out of the way. Aliens jump her, trying to kill and trying to protect the Newborn, but she blows them out of the air. It feels pretty good.

A few shots go wild and punch big holes in the side of the tank. Light streams in through them. Ripley sees—and continues firing in that direction. She makes a big enough hole that she can run and smash through to—

SEQ. 80—INT. BY TANK—CONTINUOUS

Rolling and coming up in an instant. She looks around her. No exit this way, but there is a vent above her.

The Newborn's head lunges at her, the small hole making it impossible for the creature to get all the way through. But it wriggles, pushing . . . it's definitely not in the mood for love anymore.

Ripley jumps up, grabbing a pipe, and kicks open the vent grate, throwing herself up the vertical shaft with astonishing ease.

SEQ. 81—INT. *BETTY*—CONTINUOUS

Vriess is scrambling away, knocking things over to avoid the baby alien.

Johner shoots at the creature as it speeds toward Vriess.

> CALL
> Don't shoot it! *Betty*'s hull is too thin!

> JOHNER
> Look out!

It knocks over canisters as it speeds across the table and behind some instruments.

> VRIESS
> Where'd it go!?

It leaps out of the darkness and heads straight for Call—she stumbles back, trips—it comes at her, leaps right at her face, she pulls her hand back—and flicks her wrist. The stiletto pops out as the creature flies at it, the blade slides right into its mouth, running eight inches through its innards before it pokes out the other end.

Blood starts to burble out, and Call scrambles for the door. One drop falls and she catches it, letting it burn through the palm of her hand. She gets outside just as the creature wriggles and finally falls free, the stiletto melting inside it.

SEQ. 82—INT. VERTICAL AIR SHAFT—CONTINUOUS

Ripley is climbing up the cramped vent with the speed and grace of an alien.

Unfortunately, so is the Newborn, twenty feet below her.

Ripley grabs a pole and her hand begins to steam, it's so hot. She cries out, lets go . . . then looks down. Grabs the pole again and, ignoring the searing agony, pulls, pulls . . . rips it out of the wall, burning steam gushing out below her, barely slowing down the Newborn.

She continues climbing, then kicks through a grate.

SEQ. 83—EXT. SPACE—CONTINUOUS

The Auriga *races toward:*

Earth. But not as we've seen it.

The planet is still blue, but almost two thirds of it is obscured by a giant orbiting latticework of metal, a partial shell that rotates slightly faster than the planet itself.

The Auriga *heads for a section of exposed Earth. Not long now.*

SEQ. 84—INT. COCKPIT—CONTINUOUS

The four remaining crew are in motion, trying to get the ship mobile. Call moves to the controls at the navigator's chair, behind Vriess.

JOHNER
Call, is the *Betty* prepped?

CALL
She's hot. I'll shut the *Auriga*'s airlock. Pull the holding clamps on your mark.

VRIESS
(looking about him)
Right . . . Just need to . . . find uh, the vertical thrust
lock . . .

DISTEPHANO
(worried)
You guys can fly this thing, right?

SEQ. 85—INT. ANTECHAMBER—CONTINUOUS

Ripley drops to the ground and heads for the dock.

CALL/SHIP
Airlock doors closing. Stand clear.

RIPLEY
No!

*She doesn't bother to try the door, she hurls herself through the
window, landing—*

SEQ. 86—INT. DOCKING BAY

In a hail of glass.

ANGLE: MAGNETIC CLAMPS—

As they begin to pull away from the Betty.

Ripley is on the platform that runs the length of the dock. The
Betty *is barely visible past the far end, sinking into the airlock as
the massive inner doors slide slowly shut over it.*

RIPLEY
No!!

A slam against the metal door behind her tells her the Newborn is here. She picks herself up and runs—and she can run fast. Faster than any human can.

ANGLE: THE CLAMPS

The last of them pull away.

Ripley speeds across the platform, faster, faster, the Betty *sinks out of sigts as the airlock doors move closer together, fifteen feet apart, ten . . .*

Ripley reaches the edge of the platform and leaps, just hurls herself off the platform, sails through the air, inhumanly far—thirty, forty feet, and down, the airlock doors thirty feet below her, almost closed. She drops right through just before they close, falls another fifteen feet and lands—wham!!—on top of the Betty.

SEQ. 87—INT. COCKPIT—CONTINUOUS

They hear the thud of Ripley's landing.

> DISTEPHANO
> What is that?

> JOHNER
> Whatever it is, we'll shake it off!

SEQ. 88—INT. OUTSIDE THE *BETTY*—CONTINUOUS

Ripley pulls herself to the hatch door, opens it. We see something moving behind her—just a glimpse of it—as she pulls herself in.

SEQ. 89—INT. CARGO BAY—CONTINUOUS

She starts shutting the hatch behind her.

SEQ. 90—INT. COCKPIT—CONTINUOUS

A light indicates the open hatch. Johner looks at it.

                    JOHNER
        The goddamn hatch!

                    CALL
        Where?

                    JOHNER
        Cargo bay!

                    VRIESS
        How did it—

                    CALL
        Son of a bitch . . .

She has crossed to a small bank of video monitors, and sees Ripley approaching.

                    CALL
        Ripley.

                    JOHNER
        Where?

Here, as she comes into the cockpit and moves purposefully to the front.

                    CALL
        Ripley . . .

RIPLEY
Hi.

DISTEPHANO
Man, I thought you were dead.

RIPLEY
I get that a lot. Why are we still here?

VRIESS
I'm just . . . uh, finding the manual override—is that it?

RIPLEY
Oh, for Christ's sake …

She pushes Johner out of the way and hops into the second pilot's chair.

JOHNER
What do you know about flying these?

RIPLEY
Are you kidding? This piece of shit's older than *I* am.

She starts hitting buttons, flipping switches—without even looking at half of them.

RIPLEY
How long till we hit atmosphere?

CALL
A few minutes.

JOHNER
This thing'll buck like a mule in atmo.

RIPLEY
I can handle it. Just open the goddamn airlock.

DISTEPHANO
We still got breach! Look! The hatch!

RIPLEY
I shut it.

JOHNER
Yeah, good job—

CALL
I got it.

She takes off toward the back.

SEQ. 91—INT. CARGO BAY—A MOMENT LATER

*Call rushes in and goes to the hatch. She starts closing the door—
but it won't quite close—she examines the locking mechanism—it's
bent out of shape, as though the door has been forced open.*

CALL
Dammit . . .

*She looks around her. The cargo bay is fairly dark, and she peers
into the shadows. Takes a step that way and comes back with an
iron bar. Slips it between the bent mechanism and pulls. Slowly the
lock bends back into a semblance of its normal shape.*

She drops the bar and tries forcing the door home. It almost goes.

Close on: Call

The camera holds tight on Call *as she steps back—and whips across with her as she slams her shoulder into the door. Moves back— and again to the door for a second hit. Moves back, and the Newborn is right there, inches from her.*

He closes the door for her.

SEQ. 92—INT. COCKPIT—CONTINUOUS

                              RIPLEY
         Now!

She hits a switch and the Betty *jerks down, everyone holding on as—*

SEQ. 93—EXT. *AURIGA*—CONTINUOUS

The Betty *flies down out of the airlock, veering off from the huge Auriga.*

SEQ. 94—INT. CARGO BAY—CONTINUOUS

Call is knocked off balance, but so is the Newborn as crates and parts fall around it from the sudden jerk.

Call scrambles away frantically, over parts, finally crawling under a machine. She waits in the dark, a wall keeping her from going any further.

Angle: Call's pov

Looking out from under the machine. No alien.

Suddenly its face drops into frame, hissing. Call flattens herself against the wall as the Newborn reaches its scarecrow arm toward her, reaching, reaching incredibly far—

But not far enough. Its fingers grab air inches from Call's silent face.

SEQ. 95—EXT. SPACE—CONTINUOUS

Far away, we see the Auriga *heading for the planet. It has hit atmosphere and is on fire.*

It hits a big blue patch (i.e. ocean) and crashes with a huge explosion. A moment later the Betty *roars through frame, headed for a different spot.*

SEQ. 96—INT. COCKPIT—CONTINUOUS

The ship is bucking, but Ripley keeps firm hold on the joystick. A panel sparks, smokes.

> JOHNER
> Shit!

> VRIESS
> Reroute it!

Johner gets on his knees and starts prying open a panel.

> RIPLEY
> This thing is gonna fall apart!

> DISTEPHANO
> (checking readout)
> Pressure's unstable!

> VRIESS
> Get Call. Tell her to turn on the auxiliary pumps in the bay.

Rifle slung over his back, Distephano takes off.

JOHNER
What's the bitch doing—taking a nap?

SEQ. 97—INT. CARGO BAY—CONTINUOUS

Call shrinks futher back as the angry Newborn struggles to get closer.

ANGLE: CALL'S KNIFE—

As she slips it out of her pocket.

ANGLE: DISTEPHANO—

Runs into the bay, calling out at the same time:

DISTEPHANO
Call?

At the end of the room, Call and the Newborn hear it. The Newborn turns, smiles, and starts slithering out from under the machine.

Call swings with the knife, shoving it through the Newborn's hand and burying it in the machine—just before the creature can get its arm out.

The Newborn screams—

Door shut, Distephano turns at the sound—

And Call slips out the side, comes up yelling:

CALL
Get out!

Distephano comes toward her instead, pulling the rifle around—

ANGLE: THE NEWBORN'S HAND

As the acid of its blood eats through the knife—

Distephano comes to the Newborn, hesitates just a second at the sight of it, then aims swiftly—

ANGLE: THE HAND

As the blood finishes its work, the end of the knife dropping away and the hand pulling free.

The Newborn comes up between Distephano and Call, shooting forward with astonishing swiftness. It grabs the barrel of the rifle and before Distephano can squeeze off a single shot it shoves the stock right through his torso. His eyes widen with death.

The Newborn drops him, turns back to Call.

SEQ. 98—INT. COCKPIT—CONTINUOUS

Johner is on his back, buried in wiring. Things are not going well.

> VRIESS
> Patch it through the servo!

> JOHNER
> Hey! This is supposed to be your job, rolly-boy. I mostly just hurt guys.

Vriess hits the intercom button.

> VRIESS
> Call! Get back up here!

No answer.

VRIESS
Call!

ANGLE: RIPLEY

She just knows.

She sits up straight, all attention, for a moment. Then she's out of the chair and gone.

VRIESS
Ripley!

He grabs at his joystick, trying to bring the bucking ship under control.

SEQ. 99—INT. CARGO BAY—CONTINUOUS

Call is cornered, staring at the Newborn with grim terror. It is having fun. It reaches for her.

Ripley enters, calls to it:

RIPLEY
Hey!

The Newborn spins, looks at her.

Ripley stands above the dead Distephano. He is on his side, the gun sticking out of his chest. With appalling calmness, Ripley puts her foot on his shoulder, pushing him onto his back so the rifle swings up in the air—and she grabs it without bending over, pulls it out of his chest with a hollow plop, trains it on the Newborn. It all takes less than a second.

But the Newborn is fast, too, grabbing Call and pulling her around as a shield. Mexican standoff.

                          CALL
Ripley . . . Shoot.

ANGLE: RIPLEY

She stares at her, then shifts her gaze to the alien's face.

ANGLE: THE NEWBORN—

*Returns her gaze. Something seems to pass between them. A strange
little smile creeps about Ripley's mouth—mirrored on the
Newborn's.*

Ripley puts the rifle down.

                      RIPLEY
                     (softly)
Come on. Yes . . .

*She could be speaking to a child—or a lover. The Newborn lets go of
Call, never taking its eyes off Ripley.*

Call scrambles away. Call addresses her without looking at her.

                      RIPLEY
Get out.

*Ripley moves toward the Newborn slowly—and it moves toward
her. Call backs away to the entrance, eyes on them, not
understanding.*

                      RIPLEY
Come on . . .

*They reach each other, standing close. The Newborn reaches out
and caresses Ripley's head with its giant hand. Ripley returns the
gesture, running her hand along the Newborn's smooth skull,
causing the Newborn to hiss, its tongue sliding out and twitching
at her.*

ANGLE: CALL—

Has not quite left, is staring with fascination at this grotesque dalliance.

ANGLE: CALL'S POV

Ripley and the Newborn stand close, framed in the large window behind them.

Ripley continues to run her hand along the Newborn's head—finding its mouth, and running her palm along the edge of its teeth. Hard.

The Newborn shakes with eagerness as Ripley pulls her hand away. She looks at it:

ANGLE: HER PALM—

Is cut, and filling with blood.

She looks back up at the Newborn, grim determination filling her eyes.

She waves her arm, spilling her blood on the window nearby.

ANGLE: THE BLOOD—

Hits the window and begins eating through.

The Newborn looks at the window, at her. Gets the idea. It snarls, grabbing her—

—the blood eats a hole through—

—and the Newborn is sucked toward it, slams against the window, cracking it further. Ripley and other objects in the room are pulled as well, though not with as much force.

Call pulls herself around the corner. She smashes her hand through a glass emergency cabinet, pulling out parachutes and medical sundries, looking for something.

ANGLE: THE NEWBORN—

Screams as it begins to be sucked through the tiny hole.

SEQ. 100—INT. COCKPIT—CONTINUOUS

Vriess fights the controls. Johner comes up next to him and grabs the joystick as well, pulling up.

SEQ. 101—EXT. BETTY—CONTINUOUS

As it streaks through space toward the Earth's atmosphere.

SEQ. 102—INT. CARGO BAY—CONTINUOUS

It's not pretty. More and more of the Newborn is literally being sucked through itself. Ripley is trying to fight her way out of the room. A toolbox dislodges itself, slamming her in the head on its way to the window.

Air is being sucked through the pitiful creature's eye socket. The window looks about to blow completely out—

Call pulls out a strap and clips, hooks it to the wall and to her belt. She comes around the corner in time to see:

The last of the Newborn, flesh and bone in a hideous pile. The sight of it stops her.

Then the window explodes.

Ripley is jerked across the room—so is Call, who grabs Ripley just before she herself is jerked back by the strap. Call tries desperately to keep her grip on Ripley's hand—

SEQ. 103—EXT. BETTY—CONTINUOUS

As it hits the atmosphere—

SEQ. 104—INT. COCKPIT—CONTINUOUS

As the two men are actually gaining control of it—

SEQ. 105—INT. CARGO BAY—CONTINUOUS

As the pressure equalizes, dropping the two women to the ground hard. They pull themselves away from the window, now whipping both with wind and with the fire of re-entry. They stare out at it, breathing hard.

SEQ. 106—INT. COCKPIT—CONTINUOUS

Johner lets go, Vriess handling it easily. Johner grabs Vriess and kisses him right on the lips.

JOHNER
So, what do you want to do tomorrow?

SEQ. 107—INT. CARGO BAY—CONTINUOUS

The two women move slowly to the window, a somewhat spectacular view of the Earth passing below them. They stare out at it together.

RIPLEY
So you did it. You saved the Earth.

CALL
You disappointed?

Ripley smiles slightly, but doesn't answer. They look out at the Earth.

CALL
It's beautiful. I didn't expect it to be.

RIPLEY
Never been to Earth?

CALL
No. What do we do?

RIPLEY
I don't know . . . I'm a stranger here myself.

We hold on the two of them, staring into the distance.